Penny,
To a person who is
really in touch with
her "mystical self",
Keep on enlightening others!
All my best,
Sharon Baker

Healing With Hands:
Miracles, Inspiration and Science

Reiki and Other Related Energy Therapies:
A Holistic Approach to Healing

Sharon Baker, R.N., Reiki Master

D1452521

Imlay City, Michigan

Copyright © 2005 by Sharon Baker

All rights reserved. No part of this book may be used or reproduced in any manner whatsoever without written permission except in the case of brief quotations embodied in critical articles and reviews. Printed in the United States of America.

For more information address: Sharon Baker
P.O. Box 314
Imlay City, MI 48444
sbakerhealer@aol.com

Cover photograph by Ashok Rodrigues
Author photograph by Megan Baker

Library of Congress Cataloging-in-Publication Data

Baker, Sharon, 1947-

Healing with hands : miracles, inspiration and science : Reiki and other related therapies : a holistic approach to healing / Sharon Baker.

p. cm.

ISBN 0-923568-65-4

1. Reiki (Healing system) 2. Alternative medicine. I. Title.

RZ403.R45B35 2005

615.8'51—dc22

2005000764

To Uncle Leonard Brandt, a graduate of Chicago School of Chiropractic and Drugless Physicians (1948), and in memory of his daughter, Shyla, who chose the same path. God bless you both.

Also, to healers throughout the ages, especially to those who suffered at the hands of ignorance.

Contents

Acknowledgements

Annick Hivert-Carthew: My guide, consultant, and friend who offered support and a wealth of advice—from friendly to professional. Thank you so much, from the bottom of my heart! I could not have completed this book without you! I see your professional touch everywhere. Many blessings to you and may your published books continue to flourish.

Ron and Pat Komondy: I honor you both for demonstrating and preserving ancient ceremony as you are doing and giving me permission to write about it in "Karen's Way." May *The Great Mystery* always be with you, Aho.

Dr. Annette Mullett: Thank you for teaching "Quantum Healing: Science and Essence." That weekend with MHNA was exactly what I needed. I respect and admire your courage to take a stand for what is right. May we always be friends and may you pick up your pen soon! The truth is out there; we must show it.

Sister Suzanne Skowronski, R.N., M.A., Healing Touch practitioner: I appreciate your kind words and support. Thanks for your insight into energy theories, for helping me with this title, and for all the scientific studies you provided for me. Keep up the good work, especially as an energy healer. You are a respected role model!

To Dr. Usha Srivastava, Professor of Hindi: Thank you for your input and explanation of Hinduism, Buddhism, and views on karma and reincarnation. I am grateful to you for sharing your beautiful home, garden, and *excellent Indian food*. Your friendship has been very dear to me.

To Rev. Tom N. Frederick, Unity Minister, hospital chaplain: Thank you for doing God's work every day, your input in the chapter "Energy from God," and your interest in Reiki.

To Rev. Sue Camaiore, Spiritual Care Coordinator: for your kind support and most interesting input regarding "Energy from God" and others. You really helped me expand my view on gratitude and the unconditional love from God.

Alexandra Jett, R.N., friend, and former work comrade: I'm grateful for all of your encouraging words through the years. I appreciate all of the insightful tidbits you provided for the book via e-mail or over dinner. You were always there when I needed a great spirit!

To Rebecca, Medicine Owl, Ojibwa friend and guide: Thank you for opening the door, then giving me a gentle push toward the Vision Quest, for sharing your ceremonial pipe, your gifts, your songs, and your ancient ways. Thanks for *talking me in* and advising me on the meaning of the hawk after the quest. It was life-changing!

I am eternally grateful to all my clients, my teachers, who allowed me to write your stories. I congratulate you for moving forward on your healing path, not always an easy task. I thank you and may good health prevail.

Thank you to the readers of the first manuscripts, for your time and effort in helping me with corrections and clarifications: Rory McPherson, Wendy Marvin, Linda Grabda, Alexandra Jett, Kelly Spradlin, Sue Hayden, Usha Srivastava, and Maureen Elliott.

Thank you to my favorite little store, *Angel Treasures*, Rochester, Michigan, where Angels reside, in human and spiritual form. You can always find a positive message there.

Many Blessings to my husband, Todd, and my daughter, Megan: Like it or not, you never said *no* and you *read and read*. Thanks, Meg, for all the computer assistance—you prevented many disasters!

Introduction:
How I Came to be a
Reiki Master

I remember the exact day my thoughts about conventional healing shifted. I was the charge nurse on a hospital oncology unit. One day, while working on my unit and preparing to infuse another IV, I held a bag of chemotherapy tightly in my right hand. As I reached for the IV tubing with my free hand, I spotted a medical magazine on the counter nearby. On the cover, in bold print, it read, *"Energy Healing has been shown to reduce the size of tumors in a recent study."* It immediately awoke my interest. What was this "Energy Healing" about and if, indeed, it reduced tumors, could we practice it in my department?

For years, I had felt that something was missing from Western medicine. I didn't know exactly what, but vital aspects of mind and spirit were noticeably absent in the type of harsh chemical treatments I was currently administering. I was always on the lookout for ways to alleviate the patient's mental and physical discomfort. I had often asked myself: Is there a better way, a more holistic approach to treating our patients?

I couldn't wait for my lunch break to read the whole article. After I read the journal, I was so drawn to the research and extraordinary stories of reducing the size of tumors with the use of *healing hands therapy* that I wanted to learn more.

I searched for places to study this type of intervention and a month later enrolled in a class called "Therapeutic Touch" at Michigan State University. That was the beginning of a long journey of discovery into the world of healing mind, body, and spirit. A powerful and new dimension of healing was revealed to me, one I never knew existed.

In class I learned that healing with hands is the *oldest method of healing known to mankind*. It is approximately 5,000 years old in written history and 12,000 years old in pictorial history. It has been with us since the beginning of time and probably will never leave. It has been practiced universally by every race, religion, color, and creed for centuries. Since it is part of our divine inheritance, it is innate in all of us: A mother pats the back of her crying child, and we place our hands on our head for a headache or on our stomach for stomachache.

After taking Therapeutic Touch, I went home and began using it right away on my family. At the time my husband suffered from back pain due to a recent work injury. I did a twenty-minute treatment for him, and he immediately noticed a decrease in pain.

The following week, I used it on my nine-year-old daughter, who was having migraine headaches. She, too, got relief. I had a long history of insulin-dependent juvenile diabetes. Within two weeks of doing Therapeutic Touch on myself, I reduced my night dose of insulin by one-third. It was amazing! Such things had never happened to me before.

I was convinced there really was something powerful to this therapy.

I began my journey and advanced one class at a time. I had many teachers. Ten years after taking Therapeutic Touch, I took several consecutive classes of Reiki, and completed to the Master level within a year. I also took other energy-based classes, such as Craniosacral Techniques, Polarity, and Reflexology. I joined the Michigan Holistic Nurses Association, and listened to accredited speakers at Providence Hospital in Southfield, Michigan every month. I attended many lectures exploring holistic modalities such as acupuncture, yoga, homeopathic remedies, medical hypnosis, dream interpretations, complementary approaches to pain management, and guided imagery. I am now vice president of the organization, and feel committed to promoting credible and useful information for the general public, nurses, and other health care professionals.

At the time of my awakening to holistic healing methods, general medicine was hesitant to incorporate "healing hands therapies" in traditional treatment. Because this approach was so important to me, I decided to open my own practice. After years of teaching and experiencing many astonishing healing sessions with clients, I am compelled to share their inspiring stories—to help spread the word about energy therapies, especially Reiki. I chose Reiki as the main modality because it is easy to learn, effective, and gaining widespread respect. My aim is to help people understand what Reiki is and does, and clear up confusion, ignorance and prejudices regarding this and other related therapies.

The idea of this book came to me in the form of a dream a few years ago. I saw a book and its contents, directing me to write about *Healing with Hands*. The dream haunted me time and time again, always with the same theme. I finally jotted it down, and at last acknowledged the fact that I might be receiving spiritual guidance and formed the concept of this book. Uncanny events of divine timing, higher messages, and the personal accounts of clients proved my intuition right. They gave me all the information I needed to complete this text.

Because of so much skepticism, I decided to begin the book with scientific evidence supporting its theory, then follow with easy-to-understand explanations of ancient philosophy, practice, and personal accounts.

I hope this book will bring gentle enlightenment to the new reader and enduring empowerment to the already-practicing therapist.

Scientific Basis for Reiki and Other Energy Therapies

Currently, almost half of all adult Americans visit an alternative practitioner annually, spending over $13.7 billion[1], which exceeds the number of out-of-pocket visits to mainline physicians. Western medicine is beginning to understand the reason why. A national survey by Dr. John Austin of Stanford University states that technological medicine is not enough—people want their medical care grounded in spirituality and life meaning.[2]

Over the past fifty years, Western medicine has advanced and made us think we could cure ourselves just by using drugs and surgery. But *these ways are not healing us at the core.* Often, we can be left with side effects from our present treatments. Take a look at what has happened with some medication. Vioxx, for example, a popular new medication for arthritis, was carefully designed so it would *not* cause

---

[1] *Manifesto for a New Medicine*, Dr. James S. Gordon, 1996.

[2] *Reinventing Medicine*, Dr. Larry W. Dossey, 1999.

1

abdominal irritation and bleeding. Although the stomach problem was corrected, it left consumers with new and much more dangerous side effects—a greater risk for strokes and heart attacks. It was taken off the market! These kinds of challenges have motivated us to look "outside the box" for more answers.

Many scientists are now looking deeper into how energy therapies work and how they benefit us. Examples of energy therapies are: Therapeutic Touch, Reiki, Healing Touch, Native American shamanism, Craniosacral Therapy, polarity, Qigong, acupuncture, acupressure, and some forms of chiropractic. All of these therapies have one thing in common: They bring expansion and balance to the human energy field and we generally use our hands to help do it. Our hands are like magnets and draw and move this *chi, ki,* or *prana* (same energy) into and through the client's body, leaving it renewed and balanced, stimulating natural immunity when the treatment is done. Therapists also have the *intention* to help heal, which assists in directing energy.

Theories about energy fields are based on centuries of Eastern observation and experience. If you could see these fields, imagine yourself looking at numerous layers of various colors and patterns that extend out as much as fifteen feet or more from your body. They are vibrational, electrical, and magnetic, and the same force is transferred through your hands. This higher energy that moves around and through the physical body is associated with health and illness. Physical, emotional, and mental imbalances first manifest in the fields around us, and can cause a block or a decrease in size and color in a predictable way. For example, prejudice and unacceptance of others are emotions that darken and close the heart center (chakra) in the same manner. These disturbances can create dis-ease at the location of the block. Years of unacceptance may manifest as chest pain and eventually heart damage. When the block is removed through movement of human hands, intention, acupuncture needles, or pressure points on the body, the flow and balance of *chi* energy improves, thus helping the body to heal itself. In reality, all healing is self-healing (Hippocrates). The patient also needs to deal with his or her feelings, attitudes, and emotions to prevent the old pattern from returning.

It is important to note, *acceptance of others* does not mean we should invite those who would *harm* us to dinner! We can separate ourselves and step away from negative vibrations without holding on to abhorrence.

"Energy medicine comes down to basic physics," according to Dr. James Oschman.[3] Energy therapies are supported by the laws of physics. For example, Oschman quotes, "Gauss' Law and Maxwell's Law state, *'Wherever an electrical current flows, there is a magnetic field in the space around the tissue.'*" Everything alive has electrical impulses, and therefore is magnetic, too. It is very clear that we are electrical beings when we have an EEG or EKG and we can actually see recorded electrical patterns in our bodies. Gauss' and Maxwell's laws, along with Albert Einstein's Theory of Relativity, which shows all matter can be converted into energy, provide the present scientific foundation for energy therapies. After establishing this basis we are just beginning to examine how Reiki and others work.

To further detect and measure electromagnetic fields around the body, scientists at Massachusetts Institute of

---

[3] *Energy Medicine: The Scientific Basis of Bioenergy Therapies,* Dr. James Oschman, 2000.

Technology, led by Dr. John Zimmerman, discovered a device called a SQUID (Superconducting Quantum Interference Device). They also used it to study the hands of trained healers, and found strong magnetic fields are created there, too, measuring up to 300 volts of electromagnetic energy. When the practitioner does his healing work, energy around him changes. Vibration and the amount of energy transferred from the healer to the patient adjust to match the needs of the client and the *latter's field balances in a perfect way.* Because these fields are invisible to the naked eye, it is taking the medical community longer to embrace them. But remember, the naked eye cannot see many things that are absolute, real and powerful—the Internet, microwaves, radio, and TV waves!

Scientists also found that the body looks like a living web with a sophisticated communication system. Every cell receives information on all activities taking place inside us—the body and mind cannot be separated and are in constant communication with each other. If you are emotionally depressed, the entire body knows, even your toes. Our cells converse with each other not only through complex systems of hormones and chemicals but electrical signals and weak ultraviolet light signals as well.[4] Electrical messages, for example, stimulate the kidneys to empty urine into the bladder and also to regulate the heart rate.

Western medicine is still based on the "mechanical" view of the human body from an old theory of Isaac Newton formulated in the 1600s. It states that "Man is a solid object only and has a clearly explained mechanical system," which basically means that the body is just a physical form and

---

[4] *Vibrational Medicine, Energy Healing and Spiritual Transformation*, by Dr. Richard Gerber, 2000

ends at the skin. All physical reactions had a *physical* cause. We worked like a machine or a clock with gears and parts to be fixed or replaced. It ignored such powerful components of our whole being which can affect our health such as *emotions, consciousness, and spirituality!* For centuries, Newtonian theories offered comfort to people who wanted to see a clear set of rules on how everything works. But new science is beginning to change this concept and recognize just how complicated we are.

Energy therapy falls in line with new science thinking. New science says there is no exact cause and effect, but is open to the possibility that nothing is absolute; so much more is possible. It thinks outside traditional medical boundaries, envisioning new causes for disease and exploring new ways to heal them. In new theory, illness is thought to be caused not only by germs, heredity, and trauma, but also unhealthy emotional patterns and dysfunctional ways of relating to our world.

An example of thinking outside the box is *quantum healing* or *Reiki Distance Healing.* There it is possible for humans to send healing energy, from a distance of even a thousand miles away, to help heal a wound. I have witnessed healing done in this fashion; stubborn leg ulcers that had been present for over two years began to granulate new tissue after three Reiki distance healing sessions.

I have seen a few people go into unexplainable, spontaneous remission from cancer after receiving Reiki treatments, and live a full life—when they did not respond to general medicine. No one could determine how. I watched a tumor disappear while a healer was projecting energy towards it, defying all the standard rules established by general medicine; *no cause, no effect could ever be rigidly measured by Western medicine.*

Robert Becker, M.D., orthopedic surgeon and nuclear physicist, has been a pioneer in investigating how energy therapies and low-pulsating electricity can "jump start" the healing process, helping bones to repair that have not mended in decades. These fields can be created artificially or *by using human hands to help heal.* Becker also concluded that acupuncture points and meridians, rivers of energy that run up and down the body, are additional energy channels to help regulate tissue repair.

Another phenomena recorded by Dr. Becker through observing healers is *information transfer* between the healer and the patient. Call it intuition, ESP, or sixth sense; he feels we have the ability to communicate without words, an occurrence we've all experienced at one time or another. This may explain how healers can "see" or locate the medical problem in the body of the patient, assisting with diagnosing. He thinks communicating with "radio or TV-like" waves is not out of the question. In the last twenty years it is fairly common to talk about picking up *bad vibes, sending energy,* or *reading someone's thoughts.*

Scientific studies have been conducted for years on many well-known healers, such as Oscar Estebany. He could, just by holding his hands near them, accelerate wound healing in horses, reactivate damaged stomach enzymes (trypsin) in humans, and promote growth in saline-damaged barley seeds.

In other investigations, Otelia Bengssten, M.D., conducted an experiment with a group of seventy-nine sick patients. The patients had diagnosed conditions such as brain tumors, diabetes, emphysema, multiple endocrine disorders, congestive heart failure, rheumatoid arthritis, and pancreatitis. Laying-on hands treatments were given to forty-six patients with thirty-three controls. The treated patients showed a significant increase in hemoglobin (oxygen-carrying red blood cells). The effect was so evident that even cancer patients treated with bone marrow-suppressive agents showed increased hemoglobin levels. The majority of these patients also reported improvement in their general conditions. This and other studies show growing evidence that healers are able to make actual biological improvements beyond placebo effect.

In some areas, the unexplored power of our mind can be seen, but not yet fully understood. One healer, Olga Worroll, demonstrated in university science labs that she can create turbulent waves inside a chamber simply through her intention. Just as impressive, laboratory slides have been published of *water* vastly changed merely by human thoughts; one study shows we can increase or decrease the pH of water by sitting across from it and *willing it to do so*. Another shows we can change the microscopic pattern of water into beautiful geometric patterns by projecting feelings of love into it. Also phenomenal, quantum physics tells us we can transfer the emotion of love into a cup of sugar-sweetened soda pop. Within seconds the beverage will taste *less acidic and noticeably sweeter*.

On the other hand, negative, self-destructive thoughts produced ugly, distorted microscopic images in water—all scientifically proven by Masaru Emoto. Since the human body is seventy percent water, just imagine how self-loathing could affect a person physically, especially over time. How and what we think magnetically attracts the microscopic beginning for conditions and events in our lives—it's universal law.

One of the most well-known and researched energy

therapies is *Therapeutic Touch,* developed in 1972 by Dolores Krieger, R.N., Ph.D., professor of nursing at New York University. When she created Therapeutic Touch, she drew from ancient practice of laying-on of hands, Eastern techniques and other methods used by world-famous healers. She created a simple energy-healing treatment where the practitioners center themselves, scan the client field with their hands, redirect the flow of disturbed chi, and consciously send energy to the client through visualization and intent. Nowadays, it is taught in eighty universities, sixty foreign countries, and practiced in over one hundred American hospitals by nurses and lay people alike. Krieger feels that all humans, not just famous healers, have the ability to help another person heal—in other words, we *are all natural born healers!* Over the past thirty years, probably because of so much skepticism, this subject has been carefully researched and has been the topic of many doctoral theses in nursing. Studies reveal Therapeutic Touch can promote deep relaxation, decrease anxiety, reduce pain, improve wound healing, lessen headaches, assist with discomforts of labor and delivery, and also significantly enhance immune function.

Current studies are being conducted on energy therapies at the University of Michigan, Albert Einstein Medical Center in Philadelphia, Cleveland Clinic, and the Department of Family Medicine at University of Washington School of Medicine. As more sensitive measuring devices are developed, they will allow science to validate, understand, and support Reiki and other hands-on therapies.

Recently, one of the most renowned cardiac surgeons, Dr. Mehmet Oz from Columbia Presbyterian Medical Center in Manhattan, invited Reiki Practitioner and energy therapist,

Julie Motz, into his operating room. Julie provides energy balancing for patients as they receive their newly transplanted hearts, undergo bypass surgery or other complicated cardiac procedures. The patients she works with have made significantly noticeable improvements. Dr. Oz has given her work credibility and continues to keep her by his side, referring to her as a *healing angel*. Dr. Oz has been named one of the top *brightest thinkers in America*, and with support like his, energy therapy will take its rightful place in medicine.

The majority of studies concentrate on physical body changes and ignore the greater picture in the recipient's life. How did energy therapy impact "quality of life?" Did it help him/her find purpose and meaning? How did it heal essential relationships or bring the patient to holism, relieving suffering and restoring balance? When asked, many recipients of this therapy report deeper healing in these areas.

Full effects of the treatments can be as illusive as identifying the impact of prayer. We have only witnessed the tip of the iceberg in the scientific investigation of energy medicine. We are still in the embryo state and have so much more to unveil.

As science moves forward, I believe Reiki and other healing hands therapies will be increasingly practiced at home, in hospitals, and medical or wellness centers. Hopefully, we will seize this opportunity to embrace all of its possibilities.

TRY IT YOURSELF! Take a can of regular sugared Coca-Cola. Pour a few ounces into two Dixie cups. Pick up one of the cups. Hold it in your hands. Now, think of someone you love—spouse, parent, your child, a favorite pet. Really feel that love. Next project those emotions into your cola and continue the process for about a minute. Last, taste the cola in each cup. The soda you placed the love into will be sweeter, less fizzy and less acidic as you compare it to the untreated drink. You have just tasted the effects of the perfect vibration. Love chemically changes our food, our surroundings, and our bodies for the better.

From the healer's point of view, unconditional love, transferred to our clients, could be the most important vibration that helps heal them.

About Reiki
Description of One Energy Therapy

Reiki is an ancient Eastern healing art. It is based upon the teachings of Dr. Mikao Usui, who, in the mid-1800s, researched sacred Tibetan scripts as part of its foundation, then received further instruction through meditation and vision on Mt. Koriyama in Japan. After he developed the complete treatment, he did years of healing work himself and found Reiki to be a powerful modality. It has been handed down from teacher to student ever since. This therapy does not belong to any particular race or creed. *It is not faith healing*. It is a compassionate human intervention.

As I have mentioned previously, Reiki is part of a large family of energy therapies. It is a cousin to acupuncture, Qigong, Therapeutic Touch, Native American shamanism, Polarity, Craniosacral, and some forms of chiropractic. One major reason why I prefer Reiki is because it is so natural and easy to use; even children can learn it.

Reiki is a Japanese word that means *spiritually-guided (Rei) life force energy (Ki)* or, as some call it, *energy from*

God. Through centering or brief meditation and placement of hands, this energy moves through the practitioner and is drawn into the body of the receiver. Intention and mindfulness are helpful in getting this healing energy to work, stimulating a "jump start" to the body's natural immunity.

Reiki theory and practice is taught in three levels. This is how I and many other Masters teach Reiki:

Reiki Level 1:

Instruction includes history and definition of Reiki. In class, students learn the formal hand positions over the seven major chakras (and some minor) to help heal a client and also for themselves (self-healing). They begin the Reiki treatment by placing their hands on strategic places on and around the receiver's head, and then move down the body to the throat, heart, upper abdomen, lower abdomen, pelvis, lower legs, and finish by holding the feet to ground the client, bringing him back to alertness. Students learn centering, breathing, and grounding techniques to utilize and transfer "chi" energy. All students receive an "attunement" or initiation which is a very brief energy treatment done by the Master for students to open their energy pathways and allow more energy to flow through them. This is similar to a homeopathic vibration or a powerful blessing. The first attunement makes adjustments in the student's physical body, thus a kind of cleansing and detoxing takes place, which creates a more open channel for Reiki. After class, the students provide treatments for friends and family and practice self-healing methods for twenty-one days. During this time, students improve their own emotional and physical conditions by eliminating negative behavior patterns and self-defeating ways of thinking wherever possible.

Reiki Level 2:

Master teaches ancient healing symbols used and taught by Dr. Usui. When these symbols are applied to the human body, they increase energy and provide emotional healing where needed. These special symbols give greater power to the treatment. Details of their use are discussed and demonstrated. The distance healing symbol is taught and practiced. This symbol "opens the pathway" to a person or place where positive energy is needed—we can offer Reiki to a living being or send peace and love to a geographic location in turmoil. A second attunement is given to the students. This vibration balances the mental and emotional body of the students, relieving blocks and bringing them in closer contact with suppressed emotions which are then released. The intuitive center located at the pituitary gland (mid-forehead) is stimulated to develop further. Detoxification and self-healing continue as insightful awareness increases. The students continue on their journey to enlightenment and continue to practice treatments at home. They also do more personal work to make positive changes and focus on wellness in their own lives. They must first heal themselves before they can heal others.

It is recommended to read many books about Reiki or take complementary classes. My favorite book for class is *The Power of Reiki* by Tanmaya Honervogt.

Reiki Level 3:

In this Master-Teacher level the students review the Reiki process. They learn how to teach Reiki, give attunements, apply the master symbols, and move "chi" energy through the body. Concepts about Reiki Guides are discussed. A Spiritual Attunement is received. A most intense experience, it stimulates personal growth on all levels and energetically prepares students to attune others. Students who take this class have committed to make healing work a real part of their lives.

Teaching Reiki is optional; do it only if it feels right. But remember, we are all teachers every day, through our words and actions. As a Reiki Master it is important to be an example, living an honorable lifestyle, reaching a higher plane of consciousness and practicing spiritual maturity. As the journey evolves, old inappropriate behavior patterns must be continually rejected and replaced with healthier ones. The Reiki treatments we provide must be done with unconditional love, for the highest good of the client. I believe there is no better way to give service to others than to offer Reiki.

The advantage of Reiki is that it has no harmful side effects and can be successfully incorporated into traditional medical treatments. It can actually enhance their effects and speed recovery. When I work with clients I always caution them to follow the advice of their doctor or health professional regarding their medical care.

Reiki was a life-changing experience for me. After I completed the Master level I resigned from a job that was very toxic to me, changed my outlook to a more peaceful and accepting one, took more walks in nature, and allocated daily time for prayer or meditation. I also worried less and placed outcomes of situations into the hands of a higher power. I set up a private practice and began to teach Reiki and offer treatments. I connected with my true purpose.

An inner ear condition—a state of imbalance that tortured me for years—left after I shifted into my new life. My body got stronger and my general health improved. Something nearly unheard of became evident: I have lived with juvenile diabetes, the most volatile type, for over thirty years now, and to this day I have *no deterioration of my eyes, kidneys, or major organs*. After so many years, according to general medicine, *I have only a four percent chance for this to happen!* I attribute a large part of my good health to the positive effects of energy therapy.

As I looked back at my own encouraging circumstances and those of my clients, the idea of this book emerged, and I enthusiastically embraced it. I began to put my thoughts in writing. My dreams came true and I became the Master of my own life. I am now certain this process can happen to you. The choice is yours.

The Seven Major Chakras and Related Information

The human body has seven major energy centers or "chakras," the Sanskrit word meaning "wheel." They are invisible vortices of energy located along the spine, starting from the base and ending at the crown. If you could see them, these centers would resemble a whirling house fan with overlapping blades. These fans move life force energy—*chi, ki, prana*—into our bodies and transform it into usable energy for cells, organs, and body tissue. Chakra function and appearance have been described in the same way by Eastern people throughout the ages.

The chakras draw energy from the trees, plants, rivers, mountains, animals, other humans, and our Source. I see this higher vibration as important as the circulation of blood to all living things, providing good health and vitality.

Since each chakra is linked to an endocrine center, it must be open for that body organ to function properly. For instance, the throat chakra must be open for the thyroid to produce thyroid hormones. Any block or restriction can result in malfunction of the organ, and eventually create dis-ease.

One example of this: If you live in an environment where it is not safe to express yourself, you may feel afraid to talk or speak your truth. As time passes, your throat chakra becomes more and more diminished by these emotional effects. Vital energy can't get into your throat center. Since fear manifests as something physical, chronic laryngitis may develop, and eventually, down the road, thyroid disease.

The chakras are more than just regulators of endocrine centers and organs. According to another energy theory, vibrational medicine, they are linked to tiny nerve bundles (ganglion) that are like small, separate brain centers that remember things. The cells themselves are able to recall specific trauma that happened there, react, and become ill.

To further understand the chakras, imagine yourself like a seven-level department store; each level has a main theme. The lower floors are related to issues of the physical and earth, the higher chakras are related to the divine. The lower floors carry basic survival products, such as food and clothing, and the upper floors loftier products, such as music, art, and information for spiritual development. If you get stuck on the first floor, and don't take the elevator upward, you cannot experience what's on the floors above you.

Open and Closed System

The chakras are affected by thoughts and feelings regarding *core issues* pertaining to that center. An open chakra indicates a positive experience such as love or acceptance; a closed chakra indicates negative ones such as fear or hatred. The open chakra will take in and use universal energy to the maximum, keeping us healthy. When closed, it cannot take in this vital energy, and leaves us depleted and at risk for disease. Ideally, our chakras need to stay open and balanced all the time, but in our humanness it is nearly impossible to attain this perfect state. The realistic goal is to keep ourselves as balanced as we can—growing, changing, coping, and by getting Reiki (or related) treatments as needed. Personally, I keep myself in tune by receiving a Reiki treatment about once a month. If ill, I increase it to once a week or more.

Over the centuries "intuitives"or "seers" from around the world have agreed on the descriptions given below.

Meaning of Major Chakras

1. Root:

Core Issues: Pertaining to physical security, basic needs for life such as food, shelter, safety, money, and possessions. Will to live—zest for life.

Location: Base of spine, perineum

Color: Red

Affecting organs: Kidney, bladder, and spine

2. Sacral:

Core Issues: Sexual relationships—Giving and receiving sexual pleasure. Reproduction. Attitude about your gender. Memories of sexual abuse carried here. Related to addictions to drugs, thrill-seeking activities, and food.

Location: Just below navel, low pelvis

Color: Orange

Affecting organs: Reproductive and legs

3. Solar Plexus:

Core Issues: Having power and control in our lives. Involves self esteem, safety, or abuse issues—

unscrupulous authority figures can remove personal power and diminish one's worth.

Location: Behind the navel and into upper abdomen

Color: Yellow

Affecting organs: The stomach, pancreas, liver, and gallbladder

4. **Heart Chakra:**

Core Issues: Relationships with friends, family, co-workers. Romantic bonds. Dysfunctional, codependency conditions. Forgiveness or unforgiveness toward oneself, others, or country. Love and nurturance.

Location: Center of the chest

Color: Green, some pink

Affecting organs: The heart, liver, lungs, and blood circulation. One of the most critical centers because it affects us so strongly.

5. **Throat Chakra:**

Core Issues: Creative expression through speaking, writing, art, music, dancing, channeling, or teaching. Feeling safe and verified when speaking out or communicating. A sense of belonging, being part of the group.

Location: Throat

Color: Sky blue

Affecting organs: Throat, upper lungs, arms, and digestive tract

6. Third Eye/Brow:

Core Issue: Inner vision. Intuition. sixth sense. Beyond logical thinking. Seeing greater meaning and possibilities in situations.

Location: Brow, middle of forehead

Color: Indigo blue

Affecting organs: Spine, brain, left eye, nose, and ears

7. Crown:

Core Issue: Connection or union with God. Divine guidance. Awakens us to our life purpose. Sacred awareness.

Location: Crown, top of the head.

Color: White or purple

Affecting organs: Brain and right eye

(Since it is our connection with God and it is not known how far it extends, any treatment for that chakra should be brief.)

Layers of the Human Energy Field

The human aura exists in four *major* layers which surround the human body. Other layers are reported but are very subtle.

Etheric Layer—mimics the entire physical body including all of the organs. It is an "invisible duplicate." Physical illness displays itself here first before showing itself in the physical body. It is composed of a weblike structure, bluish-white in color, constantly moving, and pulsates at 15-20 cycles per minute. It begins at the skin and moves outward from the body one-quarter to two inches. It is the matrix or pattern for the physical body and actually existed before the body was formed, at the moment of conception.

Emotional Layer—The second layer is associated with all of our feelings and may be linked to the brain and nervous system. This layer is associated with astral travel and near-death experience. This body contains all the colors of the rainbow, brightening with uplifted moods and dimming with depressed ones. It extends from one to three inches from our skin. Its structure is more fluid and flows more easily than the etheric layer.

Mental Layer—Is associated with our thoughts and mental abilities—the illumination brightens as we are thinking and reasoning and can dim during restful or quiet time. It is composed of an even finer substance than previous layers and extends out three to eight inches from the body. It is bright yellow, especially over the head and shoulders. *Thought forms* can even be detected by intuitives in this energy vibration. What we focus on attracts more of the same. For example, when we think our *fear thoughts,* those thoughts are magnetic and pull in more and more people and situations we are afraid of. Negative thoughts like *I never win* or *I'm afraid I'll get the flu* may be more toxic than we realize.

Spiritual Layer—As our human consciousness rises here, we experience spiritual connection, oneness with God, see the light, experience religious figures, guides, or angels, and feel unconditional love for the universe. It is the home of our higher selves, the self that knows everything about us and, subconsciously, why all things happen in our lives. It operates from the right brain and communicates through dreams, synchronicity, and intuition. Often, the logical part—or our left brain—is very punishing toward the right, making us question the validity of our mystical side, thus we often ignore important messages. This field extends two to two and three-quarter feet from the body. It is described as a glowing pastel of beautiful shimmering light and some say it is our most awesome.

The Use of Pendulum to Evaluate

I often use a pendulum before I start a Reiki treatment to help me identify which chakras are blocked, thus better understanding the core issues (thoughts and feelings) of the client's condition.

The pendulum is an ancient tool that moves in response to energy beneath it. It is a cousin to the dowsing rod used throughout history to locate water, electrical wires, minerals, etc. We can evaluate the open or closed condition of the chakra by standing on the client's right side and holding the pendulum a few inches over each chakra. It will generally swing clockwise over an open chakra and counterclockwise or remain motionless for a closed one. For some people, pendulums may swing up and down (open) or back and forth (closed). The radius of the swing may be three to six inches on the average. Usually one or more of the issues related to the center is the cause of closure. When clients are ready, I tell them what major issues I think they need to work on. In theory, these conflicts need to be resolved before the person truly can heal. The energy worker will open the chakra with the magnetism or movement of hands or with acupuncture needles. It is up to the client to continue making changes in his or her personal life.

Spiritual Guidance

I often start my energy sessions by including a message from angel or archangel oracle cards. I turn the cards face down so I cannot see them, and use my pendulum to select the most important positive spiritual message for my client. At first, because of my deeply-rooted medical background, I thought this would be a ridiculous method to help someone heal. For a while, I was reluctant to include this in my sessions. I have long since abandoned that old idea. Time and experience have shown me that important healing messages come through spiritual helpers. I still do not fully understand how this guidance works, but it has been profound and powerful for both the giver and receiver.

Energy from God
What I Believe

All energy therapies are important to me, but I am most passionate about Reiki. What differentiates Reiki from other energy therapies is its strong spiritual component. I approach Reiki from its sacred place and consider it with true reverence. Reiki is not a religion; it has no religious philosophy or dogma. It complements all religions without being connected to one. Personally, I (and many others) view Reiki as "Energy from God." This spiritual energy, God's gift to us, is accessible to all human beings at any time; we are its conduits. There is an unending abundance of this universal "chi" in the trees, the sky, the earth, and all living things. As the Reiki practitioner taps into our Source, then places his/her hands on a client, this energy quickly passes through him/her and into the receiver. Many say it is a privilege to be an instrument for Reiki energy, and I agree. Since we do not produce it, but simply channel it, we are not drained from providing treatments.

The energy exchange is perfect between the client and God and does not require our micromanagement for an exact outcome. The body has its own innate intelligence and draws this powerful and available energy in as it needs to. The giver also receives healing benefits from providing a treatment. I see that the whole Reiki concept is divine in nature, powerful, and flawless.

"Who and what is God?" I asked friends of various backgrounds: Jewish, Hindu, Buddhist, Native American, and Christian, both Catholic and Protestant.

My minister friends have helped me understand God from their perspective and their education. They have responded with a variety of statements like, "God is the ground, the source from which all beings come. It is the vibration of unconditional love and lives the fullest in our higher selves. God is all encompassing, omnipresent—one power, one presence, all knowing with no beginning and no end. It is an eternal and infinite spirit.

"We can't put God in a box and define exactly who or what it is. If we think we can fully understand God, then we don't have the answer. Some say it would be an overpowering experience, far too much for any human, to look into the face of God. Our physical nature is just too fragile to bear the glory and brilliance."

People of different religions and ethnic backgrounds have agreed that we come from the same God. Although we walk through different doors to reach it, the Highest Power has no favorites. The love for humanity is endless and unconditional.

After completing an energy treatment, I always feel *grateful* for the healing that has been provided for my client. It is important for the client to have a sense of gratitude, too.

No one knows the true magnitude of that session the minute it is over. Various improvements can happen immediately or be noticed at a later date.

Since the beginning of my practice, clients from all denominations have told me God, religious figures, or angels played a crucial, sometimes miraculous part in their healing. As I watched their stories unfold, I knew I had to share some insights with my readers. For I, too, saw God's energy, the matrix of the universe, responsive and absolutely vital to healing body, mind, and spirit.

Divine Guidance
The Call That Changed
My Life

Not long ago, I was standing at the crossroads of life and didn't know which way to turn. My present job was absolutely toxic to me. It imposed tremendous stress to my entire being and, deep inside, I knew I could not go on any longer without suffering permanent damage. I had been a traditional nurse for over twenty-five years and recently the pressure associated with my position had nearly put me in the hospital.

Standing at the crossroads, perplexed and anxious, I wondered what my real purpose and true calling were. I had a growing conflict between a deep awareness of holistic healing methods and the traditional practices I used as a nurse. I believed (and still do) that traditional treatment is important but that it is not everything. I had recently become a Reiki Master and knew I must somehow incorporate more

Reiki into my life. The more I thought, the more confused I became. I decided to talk the matter over with my friend, Laura, who has been clairvoyant since a near-death experience a few years back. Soon after being revived, Laura started to receive messages from guides or angels. I hoped she might receive one for me.

We met and I explained my dilemma. She listened to me carefully. At the end of my explanations, instead of talking, she remained silent for a while and appeared to be listening to someone. Then she put her hand on my shoulder, leaned closer to me and relayed their message, "Your Angels have just informed me you *never* ask them for help."

"Ask them for help?" I responded with a sense of disbelief.

"Yes, *ask for help*. How can they help you unless you ask? Angels and guides don't interfere with free will, you know. They are not here to take over your life and manage everything." Laura informed me with certainty.

Frankly, I was disappointed with Laura's statement and couldn't see how it could solve my problem. Sure, I believed in guides and angels, but spiritual guidance was not what I was looking for. I needed good, down-to-earth advice, something practical and immediate.

"Sharon, I know what you're thinking. Trust me. Please. Talk to your angels and tell them exactly what you want. Be specific in your requirements; what is it you need help with: What type of work is best for you? Full-time, part-time? Where, and with whom? Think about it seriously before you *ask for help*. Promise me you'll do it."

As crazy as this suggestion sounded, I was willing to give it a try. I had nothing to lose. "I promise."

"Good. After expressing your request, listen and watch out for signs very carefully. Angels have a special way of answering us. Your angels will identify themselves." She nodded her head with conviction.

Soon after Laura's departure, I made a list of exactly what I wanted in a job. Then I decided to follow Laura's advice and "converse" with my angels and ask them for help. I pondered for a while—how does one talk to angels? My self-confidence took over and I firmly asked, "Please, Guardian Angels, help me find a private-duty nursing position, a gentler kind of nursing, just one or two days a week, for someone who could benefit from Reiki or Therapeutic Touch Therapy. Show me where to go, what to do. And please, identify yourselves—I need to know you're real. Oh, and I would like to start work right away."

I began to wait, desperately watching for anything unusual that could be interpreted as a sign. Almost two days went by without a response. Will the angels answer? Toward the end of the second day, the phone rang.

"Hello, this is John Smith from *Guardian Angels Homecare Nursing Agency.*"

The words "Guardian Angels" caught my attention immediately. "Yes?" I had never heard of this agency and *never* applied for a job there. Why would they call? My mind raced, searching for answers. *Could this be a sign from my angels?*

"I picked up a flier in town about your Reiki practice," he explained. "I'm the owner of the agency and am hiring now. Would you be interested in private duty nursing, one or two days a week, for a client with quadriplegia who could really benefit from that healing touch therapy you practice? Oh, and if you could, I need you to start work right away!"

I was numb, speechless, and in total shock. My whole body tingled. In my heart I knew my *angels had just identified themselves.* I finally managed to utter enough words to schedule an interview. That evening I sincerely thanked my angels for listening and responding!

I started work the next week, and I knew I was finally in the right place. It would be the beginning of my divinely guided journey. When I met one of my first new clients, "Kate," I had a very strong feeling that something really big was about to happen. I couldn't define it, just sensed it as one does with deep intuition.

My new job was the beginning of a successful career. Within a year I cared for numerous clients with quadriplegia and saw many benefits coming to them through Reiki, such as reduction of headaches and improved muscle strength. I also began to witness improvements and occasionally miraculous healings in my private practice with the general public. Some clients with agonizing diseases became so much better.

And it all began with divine inspiration and a conversation with my angels. The following chapters recapture actual healing journeys I was honored to share with many of my clients. Names and locations have been changed to protect client confidentiality. I begin with Kate's story, "Against All Odds," a powerful unfolding of personal dignity and holistic healing.

There is a story here for everyone. I hope you find yours.

Against All Odds

It was a cold and icy December day on a northern highway when the car in which Kate was riding hit black ice and slammed into the ditch at a crashing speed. Within minutes after impact, Kate found herself lying on the side of the road physically broken, but with complete mental clarity. She instinctively realized she was in very rough shape. She called out to her family who had been in the car with her but were unhurt. As her oldest sister reached her side first, Kate confided, "I don't think I'm going to make it." She could barely move or feel anything in her body. As time passed, awareness heightened, she felt a shift, and began to feel herself slipping away. At the same time, a great peace and beautiful calm came over her like nothing she had ever experienced before. *If there is a God, I will be meeting him soon. If not, I won't know the difference,* she thought.

Against the odds, two "guardian angels" were traveling in the car directly behind her—a retired firefighter paramedic and a registered nurse. In uncanny timing they stabilized her, and then called for an ambulance "stat" on their cell phone. It arrived in just six minutes, on a country road in the middle of nowhere! Shortly after admission to the hospital, Kate learned she had sustained a spinal cord injury right below the base of her neck. Her official diagnosis was quadriplegia; she was paralyzed from the neck down. *Do I really want to live like that?* She searched her soul. *I don't know.*

At first the small voice in her head was barely audible. As time sped forward, it became louder and then perfectly clear.

I can always die later. I choose to live! Suddenly, this firm decision gave her a new surge of strength. Unbeknownst to her at the time, this was her first step in a very long journey "against all odds."

I met Kate five years after that accident. I was assigned to her case through my nursing agency, Guardian Angels Homecare, and was sure the angels were somehow at work again. I was convinced they were opening designated doors for me to go through. They often brought me to a person who needed energy healing.

At our first meeting, Kate related some details about her history. "My accident happened five years ago, and my doctors say there is little hope I can get any better. This is it! After such a long time, any further healing *almost never* happens."

Kate had occupational and physical therapy some years back but had nothing recently to induce improvement. She was not receiving any alternative therapies either.

"I'm a Reiki practitioner," I said, and explained a little about my modality. "Have you ever tried it?"

"No, I haven't, but I'm sure *willing* to."

Kate agreed enthusiastically to include Reiki sessions in my nursing shift with her.

Initially, I assessed the physical status of my new client. She was unable to stand or support her weight in any way. She couldn't rotate her body and tended to fall from side to side. She used an electric wheelchair at all times. She had only enough strength in her hands to pick up an object that weighed a few ounces. Since her bladder was not functioning she had a permanent catheter in place. Lower intestinal tone was so poor, normal evacuation pattern was absent. She also had chronic muscle spasms and hand pain that were emotionally and physically draining. Her doctor had previously ordered a "standing frame"—a supporting device to safely hold her in a standing position—but every time she rose, her blood pressure dropped so low she became dizzy and faint. Unfortunately, she could not tolerate standing, which could have improved circulation and resolved the swelling in her legs.

Kate was confronted with so many overwhelming medical challenges. After evaluating this condition, I found Kate's attitude awe-inspiring. She was positive, upbeat, and willing to explore new avenues without despair.

"You can start Reiki any time," Kate said with encouragement.

It was a big challenge. Could Reiki help?

After a few days together, we had our first Reiki session. I evaluated Kate's chakra system first. Her field appeared normal except her throat (over the spinal cord injury) and hands. I pondered a minute—Kate's power center, in her upper abdomen, was surprisingly open. It told me she did not feel personally diminished by her injury and focused on moving forward. After centering myself, I decided to include a visualization of her injured cord. I saw it thickening, repairing itself and becoming whole. Next, I saw her body recognizing the repairs and improving in strength. I imagined her saying, "I can sit up in my chair without falling to the side." Before we finished, I addressed her hand pain. I brushed the extra heat and heavy energy off her hands and then smoothed their field. I closed the session with the grounding position and thanked God for taking care of her.

After that, I asked Kate if I could do some distance healing for her. She agreed and was eager for me to include it.

Three weeks later, Kate said she noticed a decrease in her hand pain. "It still hurts but seems better."

Within three months of weekly Reiki (either distance or on the body) we observed an emergence of other improvements.

"I'm not falling from side to side like I did previously. I sit up with more strength. Hey, I can lean over the sink now to brush my teeth! Little things people take for granted mean a lot to me."

Within the first year, she experienced some new surges of tingling sensations in her right thigh, right index finger, and in both of her sides. One day she held a half-gallon ice cream container over her head. "See what I just bought!" she said. I was stunned to watch her lift it over her head! She had been unable to do that just a short time ago. We both grinned with elation over this tremendous improvement. Lower bowel tone had improved and evacuation was closer to normal.

Several months ago, Kate was appraised for a new wheelchair. The physical therapist who measured her noticed she had some mild sensation down her back, beginning at her neck and ending at her lower spine.

"That's impossible *with your type of injury! I have never seen that before!"* He immediately obtained a doctor's order for an evaluation and exercise program.

I was now certain *Reiki was playing a big part in her advancement.* It was her only new therapy in years.

Soon, a small gym arrived for Kate! She started a program to improve her strength and stamina. Next, a new standing frame was ordered, the same type she had unsuccessfully tried before. "Oh no, not the frame again! What's going to happen now?" we both said at the same time.

We decided to include a Reiki session right before the big challenge. She had always felt faint before. Would she now? To our amazement, Kate stood in her device for twenty minutes. She was so proud and happy! Not a single problem this time. What a great day! She soon increased her standing time to over an hour and a half.

"Remember, I was not supposed to improve anymore!" Kate said with a twinkle in her eye.

A few weeks ago she had extensive studies done on her kidneys in preparation for some reconstructive pelvic surgery. It was discovered that her kidneys have healed from a "reflux" condition *that doesn't ever heal on its own.* "I can't explain that," her doctor said with a puzzled expression.

If Kate were a movie star or a well-known public figure she would be on the cover of *Time* magazine or on "20/20" with headlines about miraculous recovery! Reiki would be in bold print!

Many say it is impossible for Kate to heal further—it's against the odds! We choose to remain open to the possibilities that she can.

As I see it, through hard work, divine intervention, and Reiki energy, more miracles happened in Kate's life. She has graduated with a degree that will allow her to counsel and help others with disabilities. She is certainly well qualified to be an advocate for, and to educate and empower, others with spinal cord injuries. She has just been offered an opportunity to complete even more education so that she may impact research and legislation. It was her life's dream to somehow truly help people, and in this unexpected fashion, her dream came true. She knows her greatest work is yet to come.

A miracle is defined as a wondrous occurrence, phenomenal, completely out of the ordinary, and as I see it, that's what is happening here.

"After all the things you've been through, do you still believe in God?" I asked her one day.

She responded with an inspiring story, "Not only do I believe, *I just got a phone call from Him!*"

I was listening to every word. What did she mean by a "phone call from God?"

"Just a few days ago," Kate continued, "my attendant and I were driving home after a late class. Wendy and I started talking about my car accident. I told her about my near-death story and how I was dying, but changed my mind and chose life. I have often wondered whether God was or wasn't with me on that fateful day.

"Just as I shared that thought with Wendy, my cell phone rang. I fumbled for the phone in darkness. By the time I got it my phone went into voicemail with caller I.D."

Completely intrigued, I looked at Kate and asked, "Then what?"

"I didn't recognize the number. I called it right back. No one answered the phone, but a recorded message came on, '*God is by your side. Do not dismay!*' I was speechless! Chills went down my arms. I continued to call this number over and over the next day until I got a real person. Finally, a woman answered. I asked her about the recorded message.

"The woman replied, 'I'm sorry for calling you yesterday; I dialed the wrong number by mistake. About the recording? I put a spiritual message on my machine because I thought someone, somewhere might benefit from it.' "

Those were powerful words for Kate! She was sure her question was answered. She now knows that God was, and still is, by her side.

Kate continues to step forward into new and uncharted territory, doing her best to be an example for others, in the light of truth and integrity. I continue to provide Reiki to support her body, mind, and spirit so she can rise to her fullest potential.

I recently asked Kate if she thought she could heal even more. She answered with firm conviction, "Most people would say it's *against all odds*—no, you *can't* get any better, but *they just don't see things through my eyes*. Yes, I think I can progress, and I will always, always, always be open for a miracle!"

Final Assessment

Recently Kate had a medical test, an EMG (electromyogram), which electrically stimulates muscles and nerves to see if they will react—it measures new feeling and movement she might have in her body. We were sure some nerves had repaired and it would show up in the test results. General medicine would be surprised! We were excited to get the results but, sadly, the exam did not show nerve repair, at least *not on paper*. We were disappointed! I pondered it for a while and asked the universe to show me why.

Shortly after that, I was gathering information for a Reiki II class. There was a message for me in the first article I read: A study was done on prayer and distance healing for AIDS patients and discussed at a Harvard conference in Boston. Dr. Elisabeth Targ, from California Pacific Medical Center in San Francisco, reported on her study with AIDS patients. She chose those with AIDS *"Because there is no cure for them. If they healed with profound results skeptics may change their minds and verify this type of healing."* She and her associates used distance healing techniques (similar to Reiki) and prayer daily for ten weeks. They couldn't wait to see the outcome. Instead, they were disappointed. They had hoped the test results (blood studies) would show changes in the CD4 (an immune cell important in resisting AIDS). Nothing happened—the cells had not changed.

Later, a review of medical charts revealed many surprises—the patients who received prayer and distance healing were *less* sick, stayed *fewer* days in the hospital, required *fewer* doctor visits, suffered *fewer* new AIDS-related illnesses and *less* depression. The patients did heal, but not the rigid way we wanted them to! A light went on in my mind as I read the article. That's just what happened with Kate!

I thought about a holistic nursing lecture I attended recently. The speaker talked about the word "heal." It means bringing *back to wholeness. Healing* is not necessarily *curing.* Healing for the patient may mean lining up with and fulfilling their life's purpose, coming to terms with difficult relationships, or feeling content with their life just the way it is. It can be a state of harmony and connectedness to such things as source, truth, family, humanity, and earth. I see Kate achieving all of these things, and now as I look at her through a new set of eyes, perhaps, despite physical imperfections and medical skepticism, *Kate has healed perfectly.*

Thumbs Up

My Sacred Journey and its impact on healing:

I had not returned to the earth plane;
My spirit was still soaring,
It danced to the drums
Of Lakota till morning
In my haze and in my daze,
Vision Quest memories replayed and replayed
In the cold and under the rain
Alone in the woods I would remain
Songs by the Chief, we never got tired
Wonderful heat from the crackling fire,
Smells of sage and grass so sweet
Cries to Grandfather, prayed in the heat
We merged into one, mother earth under feet.

How did it happen, what did I do?
What went on, what happened to you....?
Sang, prayed, dreamt, wept, sweat, froze, fasted and flew
Then Quested…Responded, and spiritually grew.

I had just returned home from a Native American Vision Quest, a 2,000-year-old custom I always yearned to experience, and finally I had done it! My thoughts still lingered at the remote Michigan campsite where sacred songs of the Lakota played over and over again in my head. As I reflected on events of the weekend, I unpacked in my kitchen in silence. While I drifted, a majestic hawk, my new totem, fluttered before me and landed in the tall pines outside my open window. He seemed to know, after my brush with primordial existence, I was trying, without success, to reorient myself back into the modern world.

As my enlightened spirit hovered far above my body, my dreamy reminiscence was abruptly jolted. The kitchen door suddenly swung open, and my husband, Todd, stumbled in. Slightly bent over, he was gripping his right hand tightly with his left one, and held it protectively against his chest. His face had lost its usual healthy color, and he looked as if he were about to faint. He sunk heavily into the closest chair and murmured, "Sharon, I've hurt myself!"

I crashed back to earth, "How?"

In twenty years as a cabinet maker, Todd had always been a model of safety. I was not too worried and expected an ordinary cut of some sort.

"On the table-saw. I was cutting small pieces of wood."

I cringed at the words *table-saw*. This machine is merciless. "What happened?"

"I lost concentration and my thumb went in." Todd's head dropped on the kitchen table. He shut his eyes wearily and extended his injured hand toward me. "See for yourself. I can't look at it. I think I have cut my thumb off."

As a nurse I had seen a fair share of injuries and handled them with professional coolness, but this time the injured person was my husband and for a moment my heart took on an accelerated pace.

The best I could describe his right thumb was "hamburger." Yes, bloody ground meat. The saw had gone through the bone and severed the tip of his thumb off.

"How is it?" Todd peeked at me. My face must have alerted him to the seriousness of his injury. "My thumb still there?" He seemed close to fainting.

"Yes, but in bad shape. We must go to the hospital; you may need reconstructive surgery, and the ragged site is bleeding pretty heavily, too."

My daughter, Megan, and I bundled and settled him prone in the back seat of my car. Megan drove and I sat with Todd. I wanted to slow Todd's bleeding. Knowing from experience that blood coagulates with human touch, I took a deep and meditative breath to center myself. I became quiet, and then applied Reiki energy to his thumb to provide wound stability. For a moment my thoughts returned to the Vision Quest. I recalled something a friend told me while there.

He said, "All the activities conducted here will open your energy system and make you a clear channel for Reiki energy. *It will make you a more powerful healer!*"

Divine timing? I thought, *I sure need it now!*

Coagulation soon occurred. I knew it was not advisable to apply Reiki to a broken bone that has not been set (it begins the mending process too soon), but Todd's bone was not broken. It was severed off, mutilated, with no condition for reattachment. I began to communicate nonverbally with his body, asking it to accept what happened and salvage what it could; Todd needed his thumb, or at least a partial one, to operate machinery, practice his craft, and earn a living. I also requested it to accept some loss if reconstructive surgery could not be performed. Todd was nauseated, cold, and shaky, and I concentrated on keeping him calm and his body stable during the trip.

At the hospital, he was wheeled into an operating room and I waited outside, sending healing thoughts his way. Anyone who's waited for a verdict on a loved one at a hospital will agree that one loses a sense of time. When Todd came out, he was still very pale and lightheaded, but a little grin lurked in his eyes.

"The doc said I was lucky, although right at the moment I don't feel like it," he murmured. "The whole thumb was not destroyed. After a nurse cut off what was left of my nail and cleaned the wound, I had enough skin left for the plastic surgeon to make a flap and reshape my thumb."

I sighed with relief and gratitude that the wound would not impair Todd's use of his hand.

"He gave me some painkillers and told me to start taking them as soon as the anesthetic wears off. He said my type of wound is normally *very painful,* but mine will be especially so because he had to remove dozens of tiny bone fragments embedded deep in the tissue. *He told me not to be a hero; to take the medication.*

Todd thought about this advice for a moment. "I'm leery of the side effects of such strong medicine; my body isn't used to it. I'll wait to see how I feel."

On the way back from the hospital I provided Reiki on Todd's whole body to rebalance it and keep the pain at bay. Once settled at home and after Todd had rested for a while I gave him a full energy session; smoothing, balancing, brushing the field, and paying special attention to the thumb. I used the ancient *Hopi pain-drain technique,* which seemed appropriate, especially after my past weekend. I placed my dominant healing hand (my right) about two inches above Todd's thumb and then lowered my opposite hand downward toward the floor, imagining my arm like a trough. I began to slowly pump my lowered hand, activating the process of energetically drawing off the pain from Todd's thumb. Tingling sensations immediately increased in both my arms as I held this position. I then sealed the wound energetically, and saw it heal perfectly. After a minute or two, I felt his whole body relax and it told me, "I'm without pain."

Our body knows how to heal, but sometimes we need to provide optimum conditions. Having seen Reiki's healing power before then, I trusted it to do its best for Todd and was confident in its effectiveness.

That night Todd did not need medication; he had no pain and slept like a baby. In fact he *never felt the slightest pain at all during his recovery.* I did Reiki every day for one week with the same intention: no pain and perfect healing.

Ten days later, Todd went back to the surgeon for a checkup. The doctor couldn't believe that he had healed so much in such a short time. His thumb had healed *twice as fast as normal.* "Do you need more painkillers?" the doctor asked.

"I haven't touched the original prescription,"

The doctor was amazed and exclaimed, "That's astonishing! Did you play the superhero?"

"No, *I had no pain at all,*" Todd replied.

"I can't believe it!"

"My wife is a Reiki Master and provided Reiki treatments to control the pain and speed the recovery. Here, I brought you some information on Reiki. Many hospitals use it and I thought that you might be interested."

"Oh, that. Yes, well…*maybe.*" His previous amazement

turned to doubt, a reaction I often get from conventional practitioners.

Todd and I, we don't doubt. We know. Reiki has changed his fate, my life, and the lives of countless others in many positive ways.

To this day I am convinced that I was guided to finally participate in a Vision Quest to prepare and strengthen myself for that moment.

As the setting sun cast an orange glow into my western windows, I heard the calling from sacred grounds: Grandfather and Great Spirit, we ask for your protection, blessings, and good health. We thank you for giving us these things and we praise you. *Aho.*

A Deeper Look at the Vision Quest and Its Profound Message

This information is submitted respectfully and with admiration:

Oral history, research, and personal experience told me Native Americans have done the vision quest for centuries. In more recent times, anyone—young or old, men or women of any race—with true desire can participate. Its purpose is to promote "rebirth," producing a vibrant and renewed you, or bring about visions or clarity that will offer personal insight and guidance into your life. The participant may also pray for healing of the sick or for resolution of personal conflicts. Preparation for the quest may actually begin at home, months before it happens. Sacred rituals involved vary from tribe to tribe.

Many participants create over 400 *prayer ties* to bring to camp—putting a prayer into a pinch of tobacco and tying it into a tiny cloth bundle. The ties are strung together to surround your blanket with a protective shield when you are on your quest. After arrival at the designated site, questers take part in the sweat lodge, sacred ceremony, songs, and prayers. Next, the participants spend twenty-four hours or more alone, deep in the woods with only a sleeping bag and a small tarp. It is there that you receive guidance and answers to your prayers. The world of synchronicity and signs arise, giving direction to those who will listen. Meanwhile, friends and relatives—supporters—remain back at camp where they keep warm, pray, and eat for you.

Before arriving for the weekend, I had many second thoughts—Will it be severely bad weather? Can I take the heat and enclosure of the sweat lodge? Will I be afraid in the remote woods? Will I *make* the twenty-four hours or fail? No cancellation is the policy; coping with the conditins is part of personal growth. Participants are responsible to emotionally prepare themselves and bring adequate gear.

The quest challenged me way beyond what I thought I could bear; freezing, rainy conditions intensified the experience. Brutal winds and rain blew my protective cover away and I was left to shiver in the rain. Temperatures plummeted below 32°, and I was not prepared for it. My mood swung low, very, very low. I was tempted to give up, but deep within myself, I found the strength to cope with this personal test. Once I worked past my fears, intense cold, heat, and enclosure, I became more confident that I could conquer other challenges in life as well.

I quested to gain greater insight into what to do next in my life, to understand and honor Native American ways, help raise the consciousness of the planet, and "create a better world for the seven generations ahead." Another benefit of the weekend: It would make the participants better healers; as cleansed and spiritually open conduits we would be more powerful channels to transfer God's energy.

I also asked for and received an animal guide as my teacher. Nesting hawks resided over my head when I was alone in the woods. According to native teachings the hawk was now my *totem*—and I must discover what the hawk is here to teach me. The hawk totem tells me to pay attention to my life's purpose—my most important reason for coming to earth is unfolding right now; do not ignore further visions and their meaning.

After I returned home, the hawk clearly remained with me; I began to see many new and unusual hawks everywhere—in the fields and woods all around my home. It seemed they were trying to tell me something. A month after the quest, I was walking on a country road, at dusk, when a dazzling red-tailed hawk landed a few feet in front of me. I slowly walked toward him and came within inches of his magnificent body. In awe, I got down on bended knee, and *looked directly into his face*. It was astounding, unheard of! No human ever gets this close to a hawk! Such a thing had never happened to me. In his eyes I read, *"Healing, teaching and writing are your gifts, act upon them now. Go forth confidently!"* Stunned, I bolted! I turned on my heel, and ran toward my future.

Book reference for vision quest: *Encyclopedia of Native American Tribes,* by Carl Waldman 1988 p. 193 and *Shamans, Healers, and Medicine Men,* By Holger Kalweit 1987 pp. 101-112

Still at War

Sometimes the memories are crystal clear, other times they surface in the clouded world of dreams. Horrifying images from Vietnam have haunted Jay's mind since 1967. As an impressionable young man, he was sent to fight a savage war he was not prepared for.

Jay is a good-looking, middle-aged man with a storybook family and a beautiful home in the suburbs. He owns a prosperous fabricating business in a typical American town. He is a respected veteran pilot and flies his own private plane, a four-seat Cessna. His life sounds nearly perfect—except for one thing. Jay is still at war. Jay cannot put the Vietnam War and its ugliness behind him. Despite years of therapy and a long passage of time since then, post traumatic stress syndrome still torments him. Too many painful images refuse to go away.

Last year Jay developed increasing and nearly debilitating knee, right arm, and shoulder pain that interfered with his normal activities. He could barely lift a ten-pound object.

His doctor gave him a thorough checkup, but couldn't find anything wrong. There was no *obvious* cause for his discomfort. The doctor prescribed pain medication to help him cope; however, Jay was a little afraid to rely on these drugs because they left him feeling exhausted. He had recently nearly fallen asleep while driving on the freeway.

Jay arrived at my office one afternoon, desperate to find relief. He said, "My wife read something about alternative medicine and thought it might be a good idea for me to try a Reiki session."

I have known Jay for a long time. We chatted easily about his medical condition.

"The tormenting war nightmares have come back. I'm depressed and exhausted. Even if it lasts only an hour, I need some reprieve."

I gestured toward my massage table. "Lie down and relax."

Jay lay back heavily, as if the weight of the world rested on his shoulders. As I evaluated Jay's energy field, I realized that he had numerous chakra closures—knee, solar plexus, heart, and throat. I felt strongly that they all were related to old war issues such as lingering anger, fear, the grief of fallen comrades, and the resentment he harbored against the antiwar attitude when he got back from his own ordeal. Generally, a closed knee chakra indicates the person's inability to move forward; this confirmed my suspicion that Jay was stuck in the past. The present state of his energy system contributed to Jay's pain and debilitation.

As I centered myself in preparation for our Reiki session, I stood in silence and imagined Jay surrounded by a beautiful white light. I asked our Source to enter this space and provide healing energy for Jay's highest good. I spent the next hour just being a conduit for Reiki.

Near the end, I felt a tremendous amount of pain in my hands as well as tingling and a strong magnetic pull. All my senses went on alert. The issue of self-protection came clearly into my mind. Energy therapists can easily take on the pain and negative energy of the client. To avoid that, I immediately affirmed to myself, *That pain is not mine.* I envisioned myself wearing golden handcuffs to stop unhealthy energy from moving up my arms, and imagined I was working inside a clear bubble to shield me.

As I instinctively returned to the heart center, I wondered how long that pain had been dormant deep inside his body. After a few minutes of intense throbbing, the pain surged through my hands and then released.

Had Jay finally let go of some of the trauma of Vietnam? I wondered. He hadn't been able to in the past, but this was an entirely different approach, one he had never tried before.

By the end of our session, Jay had fallen asleep. I saw his heart at perfect peace, then sought closure, and consciously placed the outcome of the treatment confidently in the hands of a higher power. I let Jay sleep for a while, and then woke him up. He was groggy and rested some more time. He finally got off the table and began to prepare to leave.

"Wow," he said. "I feel like a large weight has been lifted from my shoulders." At first he moved his arms and legs slowly, then more vigorously. "Hey, my arms don't hurt as much. Could it be possible? I feel better already."

Jay left my office looking relaxed. He called me the next day, "I don't know what you've done, but today I have absolutely no pain in my arm or shoulder. My knees are still a bit stiff but better, and I have slept a full eight hours for the first time in years!"

Jay calls periodically to update me on his state of health. "The intense pain that used to plague me before has never returned to its old intensity. I just have some mild discomfort now and then. Also, the depression I used to feel has mysteriously improved. I'm so grateful my wife persuaded me to try Reiki. I'm a scientific sort of guy; without her insistence I'd never have tried this type of treatment. Still don't know how it works, but, hey, I don't care!"

I reminded Jay to return for a few more sessions to keep his body in harmony.

Jay's story taught me, again, that many things cannot be explained on this planet. How we get sick and how we heal is often a great mystery. On a rare occasion like Jay's, the body releases its burdens, and all the client's symptoms disappear in one treatment. It cannot be explained scientifically. Personally, I have learned not to struggle for complete understanding, but to just surrender and accept what is.

Geronimo

When I first met Sarah at one of my Reiki level I workshops, she had been suffering from chronic arthritis for years. Lately her symptoms were worsening; the arthritis had flared up so much that the pain in her arms, neck, and shoulders had become unbearable. She had generalized lower-leg weakness and foot pain that interfered with walking and climbing stairs. Also, she endured frequent headaches and showed signs of early glaucoma. She dreaded becoming totally physically incapacitated and had consulted several doctors about her condition. So far none of their recommendations and treatments were giving her the relief she had hoped for. Sarah had run out of traditional options. She came to my workshop out of desperation and curiosity.

She had been a practicing psychologist for many years and, having seen numerous clients with physical symptoms linked to unresolved emotional issues, knew that there were many emotional components to healing disease. Old, unresolved childhood issues can negatively impact the body for a lifetime. She began to ponder over her own case. Did she harbor hidden and deeply anchored traumas affecting her physical health?

One day she overheard a conversation about Reiki as a healing modality that addresses body, mind, and spirit. It captured her interest. Could Reiki relieve her symptoms? She had nothing to lose and was willing to try anything to improve her life. She enrolled in my introductory workshop, and after discovering the healing power of Reiki, decided to come to my office for a session.

After I completed a routine client interview, Sarah made herself comfortable on the massage table. I proceeded to evaluate her energy system with my pendulum. Sarah's heart chakra and solar plexus were both closed. Over time, the pendulum has proven to be a very reliable tool to help me determine closures.

With Sarah's heart chakra closed, I considered possible issues related to anger and painful relationships. A closed heart chakra can constrict energetic circulation and ultimately impair movement. The solar plexus addresses the person's sense of personal power. A closed solar plexus energy center generally points to a lack of control over one's life and/or the environment. I had seen several cases involving pain in shoulders, arms, and neck related to these kinds of unresolved emotional issues. Helping Sarah to recognize the relationship of these closures with her medical condition could prove challenging.

Most people are very guarded during their first session and rarely divulge intimate concerns until you've earned their trust.

Just provide a healing space for her, I thought. Then, I asked her a few questions about her past relationships.

Sarah remained evasive and replied, "I have had a few problems with my mother."

I left it at that. At the end of the session Sarah felt relaxed and soothed. She decided to continue seeing me on a weekly basis for a while.

When Sarah returned for her second visit she happily reported, "The tension in my neck and shoulders has lessened, and my arms don't hurt as much."

Her heart chakra was still fully closed. I provided Reiki for Sarah, hoping it would further open it and help Sarah find emotional resolution and closure. During our concluding conversation Sarah offered more insight.

"My relationship with my mother has always been very turbulent. I can't remember her ever paying me a compliment; she rejected me constantly when I was a child and seldom showed any affection. She said I 'was hard to love.' I buried my pain and tried not to feel anything—I went into denial and just became numb. I had to stay that way to survive. Whenever anything bad happened to Mom she always blamed me for it. She got angry, ugly, and out of control. She sometimes handled me roughly and was at the brink of physical abuse. Everything was always my fault. I disappointed her over and over again."

As she talked, Sarah didn't seem involved in her own revelation nor did she appear to feel any emotion. It was as if she had disconnected and was speaking about someone else. I became aware of her self-criticism and lack of anger with a mother who disapproved so blatantly of her daughter.

Sarah continued, "She passed away a few months ago. Sometimes I am angry with her, but it doesn't feel *right* to be mad at someone who has died."

"Did you ever see a therapist about the relationship with your mother? I asked.

"Several. They helped some, but they really didn't understand the magnitude of her abuse. Unless someone goes through this type of relationship, it's hard for him or her to understand the mental impact of someone like my mother. Mom appeared frail and helpless, especially in her later years, but her cruelty only sharpened. I tried even harder to please Mom, hoping that one day she'd be accepting of me. It never happened. Now I feel even worse because her death gave me some relief. It's like a big weight has been lifted off my shoulders since she's been gone."

Sarah continued to come weekly for six weeks. As layers of old emotions were gently peeled away through Reiki, Sarah realized more and more of her mother's actions.

"One day I drove three hours to take Mom out to lunch. I had called her and we agreed on a time and day—I even reminded her on the morning I was coming. When I got there she wasn't home. Not a note or a call. Nothing! When I couldn't locate her, I drove back home—another three hours. It's not as if Mother had dementia or a failing memory. After she died, her neighbor told me that my mom had intentionally hidden at her home that day to avoid me. I was crushed, but this incident made it clear to me that Mom played subtle and pervasive games with me until I felt crazy. I'm a therapist and should know how to handle this type of abuse, but when it came to my own mother, it was difficult for me to confront my feelings or take action without terrible guilt."

The more Sarah revealed, the more it became obvious that Sarah had some pent-up anger and resentment coiled as tightly as a spring within her chest. I thought that if she could let go of her buried feelings of anger, her physical ailments might improve.

I listened carefully, without judgment, and waited for Sarah to come to terms with her past.

Because she was still holding on to so much buried anger, I had some concerns that Reiki might not help her. Together we decided to reduce the visits to once a month. *I'm glad we did not give up.*

After about six months of working together, a huge shift took place at one of our latest sessions. It would be the most powerful and revealing session we would ever have.

I had just completed some education on integrated guided imagery and introduced this technique to Sarah. "We often have a Guardian Angel or guide, religious figure, or ancestor who can give us an important message to help us with a present problem. Maybe you would like to call on yours."[5]

She was fascinated. "You mean try to connect with a guide or messenger; see if someone wants to talk to me?"

We agreed to try this approach. Sarah was enthused.

I began the imagery to help Sarah connect with her important messenger. Perhaps the guide could give her some insight to help her heal. During imagery I figuratively lead my client to a *"sacred place,"* somewhere special he/she feels relaxed and safe; in their garden, woods, by a beach; whatever pleases them. Once there, they may ask for and meet their guide. This figure may have an important, even urgent, message for them.

---

[5] Purpose of the inner guide: "A means of creating purposeful self-dialogue that gains access to inner wisdom and personal truth that reside in each person." *Holistic Nursing, a Handbook for Practice.* Barbara Montgomery Dossey, Lynn Keegan, Cathie E. Guzzetta, Leslie Gooding Kolkmeier, p. 242.

Well into the process, Sarah asked for her guide to appear and soon exclaimed, "*Geronimo*! That name and rugged face flashed in front of me. What could it mean?" she asked, looking confused and disappointed. "Go away, Geronimo, I'm waiting for my beautiful guide!"

"Let's try again," I suggested.

As Sarah drifted back into imagery the same thing happened. "Geronimo! I saw him again!"

"He has to be your guide," I said. "Do you know anything about Geronimo? Any clue why he came to you?"

"None whatsoever!"

I thought for a minute. "I wonder what the connection might be. We could look in my books on Native Americans, here on this shelf. Maybe it will make some sense."

I went to the shelf as soon as our session was over. The first book I picked up opened as if by magic to a marked page. I looked down and shivered with anticipation. There, in bold letters, was written, "Biography of *Geronimo*." I sat next to Sarah. "This is incredible, look where it opened." We both stared at the page. We were stunned!

"This may be another sign that we are meant to learn something from him." I concluded.

"But what? I really think we've got the wrong guide. You read."

"…In the mid 1800s…In one of the many battles to claim the West…The Mexican army killed Geronimo's mother, wife, and children in one swoop…After the brutal murder of his family, Geronimo experienced devastating anger and sadness. He was *consumed with anger!*"

"I've got it! It's about *anger*. As I see it, Geronimo had suffered and was angry." She paused. "He certainly had a good cause." Suddenly, she clenched her hands together.

"Something just came to me. Maybe he is telling me to look at my anger. It can be a normal human emotion. I've said that many times to my own clients, why not to myself? It's OK to be angry! You know, looking back at my life, I've never dealt well with it, especially with my mother. I've always been held back by the fear of rage, uncontrollable and destructive."

Sarah thought for awhile. She slowly tilted her head upward and peered at me. "That's it, as of today I'm going to take a closer look at my anger. I need to work on it! I'm sure that's what Geronimo is telling me.

"I was hoping for a gentle guide like Mother Teresa. Instead, I got a *warrior*. That's probably who I need right now," Sarah said firmly.

The week following this session Sarah called me, sobbing. "Now that I gave myself permission to be angry, I'm really feeling it! I'm getting rid of a lot of old emotions, and am going through a kind of detoxification. I've been having episodes of intense crying, anger, and anxiety."

Concerned, I suggested she find a counselor who was experienced in this type of trauma. Until then, we could continue Reiki for emotional support and energy balancing whenever Sarah felt ready.

I did not see Sarah for a few months. When she came back to see me she confessed that she was learning to cope with toxic feelings. It was not an easy journey and she "needed the emotional support Reiki offered."

I rechecked her energy field; it was more open and stable. We met weekly for Reiki sessions while Sarah continued her counseling. Her energy field was more balanced every time. I knew Sarah was on the way to recovery!

The last time I saw Sarah she looked quite different than when we first met almost a year ago. She was climbing stairs with less difficulty, had less facial tension, seemed more alive, and laughed more easily.

She said, "I've changed so much. My family and friends can hardly recognize me. Due to my lack of response, for years they had taken advantage of me. Now I react. I don't need to please everyone—I say no, stand up for myself when I mean it. I am learning to set boundaries, especially with toxic, hurtful people. I'm learning to cope or avoid them. I feel so much lighter for it. My whole life is getting better."

Sarah's medical picture has changed drastically, too. She feels physically and emotionally stronger. She has almost no arm or shoulder pain, no headaches, and takes only a minimal dose of medication for arthritis. She walks with a bounce in her step, and feels much more self-confident. The glaucoma has not advanced. Sarah is convinced Reiki has played an important role in restoring her health.

Before we parted, she said, "The journey to healing can be long and mysterious. For me, the key to the mystery was in one little word—Geronimo!"

Closing comment

Sarah returned for a maintenance session yesterday. She said she had come to appreciate, even feel grateful toward *Geronimo,* for being such a powerful teacher in her life. She is certain there are still more lessons to come. She verified once again she got the guide she needed, not the one she wanted.

Remission from Cancer
Miracles and Lessons

"I never would have tried this therapy. It's not my style," he assured me. "But I'm at the end of my rope and I don't know what else to do. The chemo isn't working and my lung cancer is spreading rapidly. I have many tumors now. The doctor says there's nothing more he can do." The man took a long look at me. I could see the pleading in his eyes. "Will you," he paused for a moment, "give me one of your healing hands treatments? I'm ready now."

My father-in-law lay back in the comfortable recliner across from me. He had always been fiercely independent, active, and energetic. He was a retired engineer from General Motors and had worked on numerous high-profile projects, including experimental aircraft. He was brilliant and mechanically gifted. As you can imagine, everything in his life had to be logical and reasonable. When I offered him a Reiki treatment after his initial cancer diagnosis two years ago, he had declined and commented that my therapy was "not scientific enough" for him—not his way. I respected his feelings, and didn't bring it up again.

But now he looked sick, helpless, and exhausted. Over the past few months he had begun to change his way of thinking outside of the traditional medical model.

He held out his right hand to show me its present condition. "Can you help me with this?" he beckoned.

He proceeded to explain that the last dose of chemo had accidentally absorbed into his tissue causing a reaction; his entire hand exploded into a red, swollen, inflamed mass called cellulitis. Circulation was impaired and the tissue was now darkening. It was so enlarged, throbbing, and painful, he couldn't make a fist or even flex his fingers.

With a worried expression, he revealed more. "The last two months of physical therapy at the hospital haven't improved my hand one bit. Doc says if it doesn't get better fast," his tone became nearly inaudible, "we'll have to think about amputation."

Many thoughts were anxiously racing through my head. Dad was in the last stages of cancer and was losing the battle. He had a terrible infection in his right hand, generalized pain, and shortness of breath with any exertion. He was frail and vulnerable. He was unsteady, had a poor sense of balance, and was falling easily. There was a tumor the size of a quarter on the exterior surface of the left side his chest and many others growing inside. During a recent hospital stay the oncologist had recommended surgery for removal of that tumor and most of the affected lower lobes of his lungs. Dad was certain he would not survive such a drastic procedure and refused. Honestly, I felt a little overwhelmed and wished he had come earlier. I mulled over this in silence and finally agreed to provide a session.

I decided to mix all the modalities familiar to me—Reiki, Therapeutic Touch, Polarity, Imagery, a few Native American techniques, and the application of one herb. An idea had come just before we began—I had some comfrey, an ancient healing plant, in the kitchen from my herb garden, and decided to make a poultice for Dad's hand. I applied the warm, moist compress to his right extremity before starting the energy treatment. My husband and I got Dad on the Reiki table. We made him comfortable and I asked him to just rest and let me guide him through some relaxation exercises first. Once he was reposed, we firmly decided to make it our intention that he would go into remission and his hand would heal. I knew from my research that thoughts can be the actual microscopic foundation for physical healing to begin. In my mind's eye I saw the swelling go down and imagined ideal health.

I was drawn to his hand first and swept the heat off the area, staying about three inches off his body. I smoothed the energetic field and held his right hand in mine. I placed my opposite hand on his shoulder, held this position, and waited for the vibration to settle—bringing his field into balance. The increasing tingle in my body told me a great deal of energy was moving through me. This sensation was a reminder to surround myself with a protective bubble—my father-in-law was energetically depleted and would draw in a hefty dose of "chi" this session. Through self-protection techniques, my own energy would not be drained.

I went on to criss-cross his body with my hands at strategic points on his arms and legs to balance the yin and yang (female and male energies). In Reiki positions I opened the major and minor chakras around his lungs. I placed my hands over his chest and its tumor and felt many dense, hot pockets of energy that eventually began to cool and soften. I used a Hopi ultrasound technique, spinning my right hand clockwise in a circular fashion over his chest, to open the lung fields and bring in more healing energy. Near closure, I continued with routine Reiki hand positions for the whole body.

I spent extra time grounding him—held his feet and visualized the color black. He had complained of feeling lightheaded and forgetful lately so I decided to gently connect him back to mother earth in this fashion. I also imagined him alert, strong, and cancer free. I smoothed his aura, placed him in a protective cocoon, and remained silent for some time embracing this vision at closure.

"Dad, the session is over," I said as I touched his shoulder.

He opened his eyes and sat up slowly. "That was relaxing. My whole body felt warm and suddenly became *lighter*—I almost felt like I was floating. Is that normal?"

"Yes, it's just the body's response to the balancing effects of our magnetic hands," I said as I removed the compress.

Then he rested his hand in his lap and we both stared at it. We were astonished as we carefully examined his extremity. His hand had noticeably reduced in size. He lifted it and made a small fist! "It feels better! My God, I haven't been able to do that for three months!" He looked at me with confusion. "I don't understand this."

I was a little taken aback myself. I thought about a response. "It's a long story and I'll need some time to explain."

My husband and I helped Dad off the table. "Can we meet for another session in a few days?" I asked. "I'll tell you more about energy therapy as we work together."

"Sure. Absolutely, we can continue."

I made arrangements for Dad's next energy session and instructed him on some hand placements, visualizations of healing, and continuation of warm, moist compresses he could do for himself at home. "It is not uncommon for people to feel irritable with a mild headache, nausea, and frequent urination. These are signs your body is rebalancing its disturbed energy field." I asked him to drink several glasses of water to help flush his system of toxins. He agreed and appeared hopeful.

I made a home visit twice a week for four weeks, then once a week for two weeks. Each time we met we did a similar treatment like our first one, and I taught him more about this ancient therapy. He was surprised when I told him Therapeutic Touch, one of the modalities I used for him, is the most scientifically studied area of modern nursing— because there is so much skepticism about it.

The complete healing of his hand convinced him that this kind of treatment can be powerful, and it can work even if you don't believe in it. Within six weeks his hand had amazingly returned to normal size and color and his fist was as good as ever.

Soon he was breathing more easily with very little shortness of breath or chest discomfort and the visible chest tumor had reduced to the size of a pea.

"I'm having an MRI of my lungs in two weeks. I'm open to the possibility that it will show vast improvement."

"Now you're talking, Dad. I think you're catching on!" I smiled. "I'll send you some Reiki on the day you have it done."

I could tell by the blank expression on his face that the *sending Reiki* idea was a little too much for him. I had to explain more.

"Another challenging theory for the logical thinker!" I chided him.

Then we talked about the Princeton study showing humans *can send intention* and positively *affect generators from even a thousand miles away.* He liked that example—it resonated with him!

Weeks later Dad reported he continued to feel better and stronger. The MRI had been done and evaluated by his oncologist. Dad had just returned from his doctor visit to discuss his cancer status and treatment plan. I met him at his home the next day.

"Well," I asked with apprehension. "What's the verdict?"

"Good news, Sharon." His face burst into a broad smile, "I'm in full remission! The lung tumors have disappeared! My doctor is both shocked and pleased. And I showed him my hand. He could hardly believe his eyes! I told him all about the energy therapy, but he just looked perplexed as he murmured, 'Never heard of it.' He admitted he didn't think I would go into remission or that my hand would get back to normal without *extreme measures*. Doc happily assured me, 'No chemo is needed now.'

"I'll recheck with him in six months." Dad paused. "I'm doing great!

"Every time I look at my right hand I still can't believe it." He shook his head as he carefully examined his normal-looking appendage.

"So, tell me," Dad asked earnestly, "In your opinion, what happened here? How did this miracle happen?"

My head was still reeling over his recovery. As I evaluated the past few months, I prepared to respond.

"Sometimes Reiki and other energy therapies work in miraculous ways because they stimulate the body's own immunity, strengthening the body to heal itself. Maybe you were on the verge of getting better, but your ailing body required a jump-start and you got it. I was the lightning rod for that to happen. I believe 'our Source' provided all that you needed through my hands. *Reiki energy* is sometimes compared to *prayer energy* that is *concentrated* and applied directly on the body—mysteriously powerful. Anyone with intention and compassion can be the practitioner. There are thousands of accounts of spontaneous healing from this type of therapy for all sorts of diseases, but that's not what makes the news."

"Well, thank you for being there to help me. I can't thank you enough. You are my favorite daughter-in-law, you know!" (actually, I am his only daughter-in-law), he said as he gave me a big hug, "I was ignorant about energy healing before we started these sessions. I'm sorry I wasn't willing to listen earlier, but I've changed my mind and *now I know the truth!*"

We decided to continue the sessions on a monthly basis just to keep his body in balance. With renewed strength, Dad was so excited about planning his big garden this spring: tomatoes, beans, potatoes, some herbs—yes, comfrey (of course)—and a host of perennials. It would be the best garden he ever had!

But before spring came, we received shocking news. Dad was crossing the field near his home when he died of a sudden heart attack. He was gone in minutes. No warning. No previous symptoms. No known heart problems. It was weeks before the grief subsided.

What happened? I thought to myself. *We expected life, the garden, the new beginning.* I couldn't believe it! *Death was not in our plan! I had made a difference and helped him get well… it wasn't fair.* In my human condition, I felt a little angry with God and the unkind turn of events.

There's a lesson here, my higher-self told me. *It will unfold.*

Months later, as spring was on the horizon, life's lessons came into view much more clearly. Now I'm certain that *within the chaos is perfect order*. All things are as they should be, and it's *not about our plan or our control*. I provided Dad with a true gift; he made his transition feeling happy, healthy, and pain free. His best friend told me it was the greatest gift anyone could have given him. As a healer, I now feel honored; this mission was my highest call.

Study at Science Unlimited Research Foundation in San Antonio, Texas. Healer Dean Kraft, in four trials, was able to loosen and destroy cancer cells growing in a laboratory flask. The method used by Kraft to destroy the cancer cells was to hold his hands near the flask and *will* them to stop living. Dr. John Kmetz reported these as significant findings. The possibility that this occurred by chance was less than one in a thousand. *"Spiritual Healing,"* by Daniel Benor, M.D., 2001, pg 58.

The Little Girl with the Big Headache

It was the onset of another headache. Natalie braced herself for what she knew was coming. She began to cry and hold her stomach as nausea and vomiting set in. The headache, slow to become painful, soon began to pick up momentum. Within the next hour, an excruciating pressure developed behind her eyes and lingered for a while. Her body began to feel numb. Then the usual oddball symptom displayed itself—both her legs hurt. She curled them up and pulled them in close to her body.

By evening, her vision became hypersensitive to light, then blurred, and a visual halo fixed itself in to torment her further. Exhausted, she fell into a fitful sleep. After the headache passed she felt worn out for another day.

This scenario repeated itself several times a week. What was the matter with Natalie? Why didn't she get some relief from these debilitating headaches?

Because Natalie did not know how to communicate her pain. Natalie was only three years old, and she had just learned to say "headaches." Until then, it was not clear to Natalie's mother, Lena, just what was going on. By the age of four, Natalie routinely suffered three migraines a week.

Lena took her daughter to the family doctor who sent her to a specialist in headache management. Natalie was placed on a variety of drugs; some helped and some didn't. She was also fitted for glasses she didn't really need. They only made things worse by further distorting her vision.

A few years later, the headaches were still not controlled, and Natalie was finally placed on Topamax, an antiseizure medication, and Singulair, an asthma medication. Natalie did not have epilepsy or asthma, but it was the medication of choice for her.

By the time Natalie was ten, Lena took my Reiki I class at the martial arts center in my town. She was very familiar with *chi,* or the energy of the body, and seemed very comfortable with Reiki concepts. She understood that the ideal energy pattern for the human body is to be an open and balanced system of chi. Lena sailed through Reiki I and decided to bring Natalie to my office to be evaluated and introduced to Reiki as a possible healing modality.

Natalie was ten years old the first time I met her. Despite strong medicine, she still experienced about twenty migraines a month, from severe to moderate intensity. Natalie was a very petite, pretty little girl who had been toughened by years of pain. She was in gymnastics and had mastered many physical challenges. After our initial interview, Natalie got on the massage table with ease.

To see a complete picture and to help direct my intention for healing chronic headaches, I need to thoroughly evaluate the energy around a person's head; small or large field, open or closed. This also determines some of my hand placements and the length of time spent on the head. It is also very important to provide conditions for deep relaxation—a comfortable, quiet room with soft, soothing music in the background. Deep relaxation can provide grounds for the body to heal itself, even more so than actual sleep.

The evaluation with my pendulum showed that the brow chakra, her intuitive center, was open, but areas on both the right and left sides of her head were closed, which made me wonder if the migraines originated not just from one side of her head, but from both sides. Natalie's solar plexus chakra was closed too. Her young mind probably had figured out that she didn't have control over her medical condition.

Natalie was a very small person, therefore I modified our session to last about thirty minutes instead of an hour. I spent the first ten minutes just working around her head. I started by criss-crossing my hands and placed them under her neck. In a very short time her spine came to a complete rest—arriving at *still point*. I felt the pulse of her spinal fluid quiet and then restart in a more subdued manner. I placed my hands at the sides of her face, over her eyes and cheeks, and finally over her jaw. After that, Natalie drifted into a deep rest, utterly and completely relaxed, just the way I wanted to see her. Next, my attention went right to her solar plexus. I laid hands there until the uncomfortable tingling ceased. I finished by bringing chi into both legs; I placed my left hand on her right hip and my right hand at the base of her right foot, then repeated it on the opposite side. I grounded, as usual, by holding both of her feet. After the session, I released her condition to the Higher Power. For maximum improvement, the practitioner must let go of worry, a difficult thing to do at times. Lena made another appointment for her daughter before they left the office and said that she would apply her newly acquired Reiki knowledge to Natalie in between sessions. I agreed that it was an excellent idea.

Natalie returned two weeks later. "I haven't had a headache since I last saw you!" she squealed with joy. Her mother was happy.

This time, the pendulum evaluation showed that the left side of Natalie's head was an open field, about two inches in diameter—a little small, but acceptable. The right remained closed. The solar plexus was still a small field, but improved. We repeated our treatment. Her mother decided to continue Reiki at home, and they would return as needed. The client always has free will and I honor their decisions.

Three months later Natalie returned. Lena reported that her daughter's headaches had shifted dramatically since Reiki had been done. She had a comfortable summer with only a few headaches a month. But, over the past week, she had had a very severe migraine.

"I think that the onset of a new school year is creating additional stress—new friends, an early schedule, and very long days," she confided. "I'd like to see these headaches improve as soon as possible."

I completed another session; after that all chakras were beginning to open to normal size. It was decided that Mom would continue to apply Reiki at home.

Natalie returned a few more times and Lena again did Reiki routinely at home. They saw me as needed.

Two years passed since our first Reiki session. Natalie and Lena dropped by recently for a friendly report on Natalie's condition. Lena told me her daughter's migraine pattern changed dramatically since Reiki. "Natalie has had only one or two migraines a month over the past year!"

I was very pleased to hear this; my growing young client had begun to experience the usual hormonal changes of preteens that can stimulate migraines. Instead of worsening, she remained stable.

"It is amazing to us that right after we included Reiki treatments Natalie went from about twenty migraines to one or two in a month. It's miraculous!" exclaimed Lena. "No medicine had that effect on her. We are truly thankful for Reiki."

No matter where parents live, they want to see their children happy and healthy. It is universal. As a parent myself, I could think of no greater service than to play an active part in a child's healing.

With every Reiki session I am always open to the possibility that the client can fully heal. That alone has power. It's the intention needed to open the first door!

Related Studies

Studies on headaches and migraines show that childhood migraines are more common than most people realize. Researchers Bille and Clark have found that 3.2% to 9% of children suffer from migraines. Relaxation as well as biofeedback may decrease vasoconstriction thought to be related to headaches. Relaxation and biofeedback significantly reduced migraines, reported Dr. Borin, an instructor in the Department of Family and Community Medicine at the University of Toronto.

According to Dr. Delores Krieger's hypothesis that Therapeutic Touch (similar to Reiki) dampens the sympathetic nervous system, her research demonstrates that Therapeutic Touch shows the first observable response to its application is relaxation. Patients also report using less pain medication and having longer periods of relief in between prescribed medication intake after implementing this modality ("Discover the Healing Power of Therapeutic Touch" by Rochelle B. Mackey, R.N., CNS, C. *A.J.N.*, April 1995, p. 27).

In 1986, Keller and Bzdek investigated the effects of Therapeutic Touch on tension headaches. Sixty volunteers were randomly assigned to Therapeutic Touch intervention. All patients who received it had a significant pain reduction (*Therapeutic Touch and Post Operative Pain: A Rogerian Research Study,* article by Therese Connell Meehan, R.N., Ph.D. from Gerber, Richard, "Vibration Medicine," 2000, p. 378).

Look Up for Miracles

Mary came for her first Reiki session desperate to find relief from the critical signs and symptoms of lupus, a chronic inflammatory disease that can affect many of the body's organs. She was experiencing autoimmune symptoms (when the body attacks its own tissue). As I interviewed Mary, I could see the classic butterfly pattern rash of lupus present on her face, its wings spreading across her cheeks, its body resting along her nose. She complained of serious arthritic-like symptoms that were interfering with mobility and movement, high fevers, and now kidney inflammation. She was gaining weight and losing memory. As if lupus was not enough, she also had been previously diagnosed with myositis, a painful muscle condition that debilitates and weakens muscles further. Although the myositis was in remission now, she was afraid it would return and felt the overwhelming vulnerability of being human.

Her lupus was advancing despite medical treatment and she was concerned about the growing effects on her body.

The symptoms became so acute that she began chemotherapy, Cytoxin, once a month. Its side effects that were most troublesome for her were nausea and generalized weakness. In fact, she spent half the month in bed due to these symptoms. She was also on a hefty dose of steroids (prednisone 80 mg.) and an over-the-counter anti-inflammatory. Her doctor told her that the chemo and steroids would be a lifetime treatment. Her anxiety increased as she became aware of possible irreversible liver damage, the side effect of long-term chemotherapy. This anxiety pushed her to search for alternative therapies that could help her. As we talked she told me about her journey in coming to see me. She began her story.

Mary started with what happened a few weeks before we met. After her last infusion of chemo, she asked her doctor, "When will I go into remission from lupus?"

Her doctor responded, "There is no hope for remission." He had estimated she would need one hundred more doses of chemo to keep the lupus under control. Mary felt hopeless and afraid. She left the office in tears. On her way home, she stopped at the library to see if she could locate any information on her condition. Nothing was available there. She then drove home. In her mail that day was a flier from a holistic center regarding Reiki. She found it interesting, but did not act on it.

A week later, she arrived at her catechism class where she taught junior-high students. Although she felt ill most of the time, being with the kids made her feel better. She busied herself right before class, and while preparing papers, one of her young students came in early. He asked Mary, "Have you ever heard of *Reiki?*"

She felt like a red flag went up. "Yes, I have heard the name," she replied with surprise. "Why do you ask?"

"I know you've been ill. I have some information for you from my father. His sister is a nun; she gives Reiki at the hospital where she works. Dad says it helps a lot of people." He handed her a free coupon for a Reiki session. Again, she ignored the opportunity.

A few weeks later, Mary was feeling especially blue. She stopped at her local bookstore to browse. Immediately, she saw a brochure advertising Reiki, and a huge light went on. Yes, it seemed to Mary, the universe was trying to tell her something. *Try Reiki.* The brochure was one of mine. This time Mary shifted into action. She called me the day she found my number and promptly scheduled an appointment.

Mary's first session was in early May. After she'd settled in my office, we talked for a short time about her worrisome medical condition, chemo, and her hopes for remission. As she talked, she began to cry, and I knew this illness had really taken its toll on her. Mary admitted she had run out of options. The chemo had left her so weak and nauseated it was hard to take care of her three young children. She explained it was becoming more difficult to get groceries, cook, or perform simple household chores. Feeling the advancing effects of her illness, Mary was starting to suffer from depression. Lately, she had a fever of 104 degrees and the doctor couldn't get the fever under control at home. She had to enter the hospital. The one-week stay helped the fever, but increased her weakness. Mary felt she couldn't live this kind of life anymore.

After her discharge from the hospital, Mary was on a mission to find new ways to improve her condition. She thought Reiki was one of her last hopes. With so many recent signs, she saw herself on a spiritual journey to try this therapy.

Since Reiki is referred to as "Energy from God," it didn't completely surprise me. After doing this work for fifteen years, I am certain God works in mysterious ways and divine guidance plays a part in making an appointment. My deepest intuition told me this would be another journey for Mary, but this time, one toward wellness. Great mysteries and miraculous events were about to take place!

During my initial evaluation, I found that all of Mary's energy centers were closed except her crown and third eye. This told me her spiritual connection and intuition were intact. My intention for this session was to provide Reiki energy to gently open her whole system, and offer her body loving, gentle support. I rebalanced her field and visualized Mary in perfect health.

At the beginning of a session, I provide a few moments of centering, and often allow the clients to call in a healer, silently or out loud. Mary called in all of her angels to assist with her healing. The Reiki session was completed in about an hour. Mary reported a sense of peace, but didn't feel anything in particular such as warming, tingling, cooling, or intuitive messages. After the session, she left my office and returned home.

Mary told me later, "I cried all the way home because I hadn't felt anything during the treatment and for that reason was sure the treatment didn't work." Then she remembered something unusual. A few hours before her appointment, she felt a cold with a sore throat coming on. She was prone to upper respiratory infection since chemo had impaired her immunity. On her way back home she stopped at the drugstore to pick up her usual cold remedy. By the time she arrived there, the symptoms had subsided and she wasn't congested anymore. She left the drugstore without the medication. By evening, the cold and sore throat were gone. Strange, that never happened! *Could I have received some benefits from Reiki?* she wondered.

Three days later, Mary said she was sitting in her living room, lost in thought regarding her health issues when she began to experience a warming and tingling all over her body. It became intense and lasted for a while. It seemed like a *delayed acceptance* of the Reiki treatment. The sensation was very strong for five or ten minutes and then faded away. Within the week, she had more stamina and could walk a longer period of time. Something in her was changing. She began to improve. Mary called for another appointment.

She came about two weeks later for her second appointment. We continued to balance and align Mary's human energy field. Mary again included her angels to help on a spiritual level. I also provided distance Reiki for Mary every week and continued to visualize Mary as healed.

In Reiki theory, we can help a person heal just as much through distance healing techniques as on-the-body treatments. There is much research, especially in quantum physics, to show we can affect the body mentally and physically through healing intention at a distance of even one thousand miles away.

Mary took Reiki level I and II from me and began to participate in her own energy balancing through self-Reiki. She developed a more positive outlook and worried less. She gave thanks for each and every improvement she experienced. We continued Reiki sessions at my office a few more times. After four office sessions, eight distance healing sessions, and daily self-Reiki, Mary began to experience distinct, encouraging changes in her body.

I met with Mary recently. It had been a year and a half since we started our work together. Mary's picture has changed dramatically. She has improved strength and remains up all day. She has been off chemo for a year! Her doctor said that because she is in remission (her labs improved so much) she does not need it now. Her steroids have been reduced to 5 mg a day—a dramatic reduction—and she has lost sixty pounds! Mary's muscles do not ache and her memory is back to normal. She can take care of her home and family. She speaks her mind now and has become more proactive in taking care of herself. And, finally, Mary has returned to work on a contingent basis. She is part-owner of her family business.

I am very proud of all the work Mary has done to promote her own healing. She has amazed her doctors who have congratulated her. Mary is convinced that one thing in particular negatively affected her health: *She gave away all her personal power*, and it left her feeling fearful and hopeless to change her prognosis. After this realization, she told me with sincerity, "Don't give away *your power* to anyone, not your doctor, your family, your friends. Do not give up on your hopes and dreams, and your visions to heal, even if others think they're impossible."

Before we departed, Mary had one more comment. "Sometimes the solution to our problem is not as difficult as we make it. Always ask God for guidance. When times get rough, don't look down or even straight ahead, always look up for miracles!"

Closing Comment

Mary may experience remissions and flare-ups of lupus and myositis throughout her lifetime. She must evaluate what is healthy and what is toxic for her, both emotionally and physically, and respect her boundaries. Her connection with her Source, energy therapy, and her mastery of self care may still be Mary's best medicine.

Case Study

"Lupus and Healing in the Philippines," by Dr. Richard Kirkpatrick, *Journal of the American Medical Association,* 1981. A twenty-eight-year-old woman in the Philippines had lab-confirmed, advanced-stage lupus with these symptoms: kidney damage, liver enlargement, thyroid reduction, and lymph node involvement. She was placed on large doses of prednisone, which resulted in water retention, obesity, and irrational behavior. She was placed on chemotherapy and other toxic drugs were recommended. The patient was not satisfied with her progress, finally refused all treatments, and went home to her small Philippine village. She chose to be treated by her local medicine man. She went into *full remission in three weeks,* and twenty-three months later gave birth to a healthy baby. No further signs of disease have ever returned.

This case again stimulates the eternal questions: How, why, and when do we heal?

Apparition of the Blessed Mother

I was compelled, almost as if someone guided me, to go to my jewelry box and pull out "The Medal," the one of Mary, Mother of Jesus—a gift I received last year from a friend. For no reason at all, except to follow my instinct, I slipped it into my pants pocket, and then headed downstairs to answer the doorbell. My client, Zita, had just arrived, accompanied by her two grown daughters.

"I'm ready for our session," she said in a soft voice.

I was in immediate awe of Zita. There was something beautiful about her. I couldn't quite define it; a sort of aura, a certain luminance enhanced by the sunrays filtering through my office window. It cast a golden hue across her face. She was tall and slender, had bright blue eyes, and nearly flawless skin.

She sat in the light, her daughters by her side, paused for a few seconds to collect herself, and finally began to tell her story.

"I've just separated from my husband and will be starting divorce proceedings in a few months. This situation has been pretty hard on me, and I've had a lot of anxiety. My daughters encouraged me to come to you; they thought Reiki might help me relax."

Having said this, she turned quiet, gently closed her eyes, folded her hands, and lowered her head for a few moments as if reviewing scenes of her separation. "I need to feel safer, happier," she stated after a while.

Safer? What did she mean by *safer*? Was she in danger? I proceeded to ask a few routine questions.

"How old are you, Zita?"

"Eighty-five."

Incredible, I thought. *Her posture and demeanor are so young for her age! How does she stay so radiant?*

"Are you on any medication?"

"None. And I have seen a doctor only a handful of times in my whole life."

Even more startling.

After concluding my new-patient interview, I invited Zita to lie on the massage table. She made herself comfortable. I centered myself and began to evaluate her energy field. I soon shook my head in amazement, totally awed by my discovery: Zita had the largest field I had ever evaluated, with the radius of the pendulum's swing approximately six inches or more. I could feel her spiritual field extending very far out from her body. Zita was unlike many elders whose fields diminish, due to frailty and illness.

No matter how far back I stepped away, the magnetic sensation of her energy field warmed my hands. In fact, I couldn't quite tell where it ended, an indication of a deeply spiritual person.

The pendulum swung openly everywhere except over the throat chakra, which was closed. The word *safer* she had mentioned earlier came back to me. Did Zita have a secret, a personal crisis she was afraid to reveal? I guessed that safety issues had affected her throat chakra.

I moved my feet to another position. As I did so, my loose pants shifted and I suddenly became aware of a sensation in my pocket. What was it? Ah, yes, the medal of Mary that I had slipped in earlier. Now, why had I felt the need to pick it up this morning? Could it have been divine guidance? My mind drifted to the story of the "Miraculous Medal."

Apparently, on November 27th, 1830, the Blessed Mother appeared to Sister Catherine Laboure in a chapel in Paris, France. Catherine described Mary as "Perfectly Beautiful." The nun was told by the Blessed Mother to have her (Mary's) image cast on a medal. The Blessed Mother said, "All who wear it will receive great graces." For those who did, many miracles were reported. Sister Catherine was acknowledged and canonized as a saint in 1947. I halted my daydream, and quickly refocused on my client in time to address her spiritual component.

"Zita, would you like to call on a healer, a religious figure, an angel, or a guide to help with this session? You don't have to tell me who it is, it's your choice." She nodded but remained silent, and I continued to provide Reiki as usual. This session, as it turned out, was anything but usual!

After placing my hands in a pattern around Zita's face, I moved on to the throat chakra, then over the heart. As I did so, the name "Mary" flashed into my mind. Not once, but several times, each with increasing clarity. Suddenly, all my senses quickened and went on alert.

Within moments, I felt a presence in the room. First, a

firm pressure was applied on my back, particularly on my right side, as if someone was leaning against me. It began to move like a warm wave down my arms and through my hands, gentle, soft, and reassuring. I was not imagining it; *it was really happening.* I felt like I was standing in the midst of a high vibration or the sun was diffusing its warmth over me on a perfect day—the depth of this peacefulness seemed almost surreal. It was then that I knew I had become a conduit for a higher being. I was overwhelmed, honored, and suspended in time.

Next, I experienced a release of some tension I had been unconsciously holding onto, and I completely let go. I was weightless, drifting in space, and imagined my fingertips reaching out and touching the edges of the spiritual plane. Subtle energy awareness occurred. There was a sudden, discernable shift! It was at that moment, I believe, that the Blessed Mother stepped in and took over.

Now keenly observant, I reminded myself: *Your responsibility is just to* be. *You are an* instrument *for her to move through. This presence is responding to Zita's call and will take care of her in a perfect manner.*

My mind was racing. Had my client called in Mary? Was she especially connected to her? Was the Blessed Mother here to assist with Zita's healing just as she had asked? Was this why I was *directed* to pick up the medal this morning?

I finished the Reiki session in complete silence. At closing, I smoothed Zita's field, placed the emotional healing symbol over her throat chakra, and finally cocooned her in white light. Zita had fallen asleep and seemed comfortable as she lay there on the table.

I woke her up gently. She stirred a little and began to sit up.

I looked at her and pulled up a chair so I could sit close. "Zita," I said, looking deeply into her eyes. "Would you mind telling me who you called in as a healer? I think I know who it was and would love to have it confirmed."

She paused briefly. "*I called in the Blessed Mother*, of course, I pray to her every day."

"Thank you for sharing this with me. I knew it, I truly felt her presence. Do you have a special relationship with her?"

She hesitated briefly before speaking. "I have apparitions of Mary. She has appeared to me many times since childhood, especially when I'm in trouble. I call her my angel. She also appeared to my mother during her whole life."

"Does she talk to you just like I am doing right now?"

"Not really. It's hard to explain. When she comes, she does not speak to me in words; I *feel* what she is telling me. It's a kind of mental communication—a knowing that takes place."

I was fascinated. Zita had my full attention. "When was the last time she came to you?"

"About four months ago. Things were not going well in my marriage. I suspected that my husband was trying to hurt me, perhaps for money reasons. I was confused about my relationship with him, his lack of honesty, and what he might do to me. There was danger lurking in my house. I didn't know where and when it would occur.

"Just before Mary appeared to me, my husband insisted on taking me for a ride late one night. To my surprise, he drove deep into the woods in frigid winter weather. It was well below zero and the snow was about two feet deep in northern Minnesota. He stopped the car on a deserted road, and turned to me with an odd look in his eyes. I shivered, suddenly frightened, and thought: *He's going to push me out of the car and leave me here to freeze to death.* I burst into tears, nearly hysterical, and demanded he take me home.

"He sat there for a few minutes, finally turned the car around, and took me home. Soon after this I experienced inexplicable symptoms: nausea, dizziness, and confusion. Where were they coming from?

"That's when the Blessed Mother came to me one night. At first, she stood at the foot of my bed, and then moved very close to me. She was absolutely beautiful, more than during previous apparitions! That night, she was bathed in a massive halo of bright, radiant light. Pure silver streamed all around her. I sat up, unable to move, entranced by her loveliness. I wish you could have seen her! She always comes when I need guidance."

"Did she speak? What did she say?"

"She silently communicated, 'You must leave your home immediately; it isn't safe anymore. You are in great danger. Go!' I did not sleep that night. Looking back, I am convinced she came just in time to save me.

"The next day I called one of my daughters. 'Come and get me right now. I'll tell you more when you arrive.' My daughter and her husband came that evening and moved me downstate. My daughters later confessed that they'd been concerned for a while."

As our appointment came to a close, I truly believe this session was more beneficial for me than it was for Zita. After she left, I pondered on the real meaning of our meeting. Was there a lesson here for me? Enlightenment soon came.

All clients are teachers, but Zita was my sacred one. She gave credence to the awe-inspiring powers of the spiritual field, and I respect these grounds even more. She also answered a question I have asked myself, especially when times are tough: *When we ask for spiritual help, does it really, truly come?* I now say with certainty, *yes.*

I have seen this client for two more sessions now. She reports that Reiki makes her feel stronger, healthier, and safer. Indeed, she looks more peaceful and serene. She also continues to verify her apparitions of Mary.

Since then, I wear the Miraculous Medal every day. Although I am not of the same religious denomination as Zita, my brush with Mary seemed to tell me this beautiful energy would lovingly respond to any of us.

Science did not and could not enter this session today. It had qualities that cannot yet be measured by man.

"For those who believe, no proof is necessary. For those who don't believe, no proof is possible."
John and Lyn St. Clair Thomas, "Eyes of the Beholder."

More Insight

The Miraculous Medal is one of the most worn and honored in religious history. According to documents, Catherine Laboure was a sister with the Daughters of Charity in Paris, France, in 1830. She was awakened one night and led to the convent chapel by a brilliant light and the voice of an angel. There she experienced an apparition of the Blessed Mother in "A Blaze of Glory." Catherine approached her and put her hands in Mary's lap and felt the Virgin's arms wrap around her. Mary expressed pain and anguish at the "evils of terror in Europe that will quickly become even worse." She promised to reappear soon to offer something to relieve human suffering. In a later apparition, Catherine described the Blessed Virgin as standing on a globe. Her face was beautiful beyond expression. Precious gems from her fingers emitted dazzling streams of light. An oval frame formed around Mary; on the back of the frame were the letter M and a cross. Below this was the heart of Jesus crowned with thorns and Mary pierced with a sword. She instructed Catherine to have a medal made in this form and said, "All who wear it shall receive great graces." Since then, millions of accounts of miracles and healing have been reported by people wearing it.

The Stand

Al came to me a little over two years ago. The first thing he did before talking to me was to cross his arms firmly against his chest and look me straight in the eye. "I'm taking a stand," he said. "I'm not ready for surgery. Not yet. My doctors are recommending a kidney transplant in about two months. My sister is donating a kidney; she's a perfect match, which is good, but accepting a kidney from another person is a serious decision; it means major surgery for the donor. I feel really bad about taking a kidney from my sister and putting her through that trauma. I've got to try other avenues first."

Al explained that all of his doctors had just diagnosed him with renal failure. On a rating from one through five, Al rated a five—the last stage of kidney failure. Al's lab results showed that time had come for renal dialysis or a kidney transplant.

As I looked back at him, he repeated. "I'm not ready for a kidney transplant and that's final. Every time I think about this type of surgery my blood pressure skyrockets and my gut hurts. The doctors are still pushing for it, and I'm going along with their plan just in case I change my mind at the last minute. I'm giving myself two months to try holistic approaches and see what happens."

"What do you hope Reiki will do for you?" I asked.

"Help my failing kidneys keep on working, and also I might as well ask for a deep healing for anything that's not 'up to par' in my body."

On the exterior, Al looked normal and healthy. His color and vitality seemed average for a man in his mid-60s. I have seen many patients with renal failure in my thirty years as a nurse. In the final stage of renal failure, the person is usually totally exhausted, has generalized body edema, extremely high blood pressure, is often mentally confused, and is literally poisoned with urine toxin. Al had none of these symptoms. In fact, he looked great!

I felt honored to support Al and was also deeply moved by his determination to participate in his own healing. Together we decided he should come at least once a week for the first month and then switch to every two weeks, which he did. Apart from our Reiki sessions, I included distance healing and prayer for him every week. During distance work, I visualized Al as completely well and saw his kidneys as perfect. As usual, I thanked God in advance for taking care of him.

When he came for treatments, I always evaluated the energy field around Al's kidneys with my pendulum and my hands every session. What puzzled me was that the field around Al's kidneys felt and appeared only slightly smaller than normal. A truly failing kidney is generally severely depleted in the energetic field. Why was Al's almost normal? It was very bizarre. Al definitely was not a typical "medical model."

Two months after Al and I started our work together, he burst into my office, full of exuberance. "You'll never guess," he said. "Just saw the specialist. He took me off the transplant list at the hospital until further notice. My kidneys have stabilized enough to take me off the list. I'm so happy and relieved!" I rejoiced with him.[6]

Al comes to see me as needed. He has maintained about the same medical picture for the past two years, and generally obtains the same lab values. His blood sugars have improved and his diabetes is more stable. He has had MRIs of the kidneys and a battery of other tests with the same encouraging results: The disease has not progressed as Al's doctors thought it would. Al's kidney specialist at a well-known hospital is stunned and does not understand what happened. How could Al feel and function like he does? The specialist feels it is just from Al's compliance with his medical routine. However, as a former hospital nurse, I have seen many "compliant" patients who could not live without dialysis or a kidney transplant and whose clinical pictures were very grim.

As I look at Al, I see him as a walking miracle.

I recently saw Al in my office. He said he has never felt better in the last ten years.

I asked him with sincere interest, "How do you honestly think Reiki helped you?"

---

[6] In 1996, Daniel Wirth's team studied blood values that were affected by Reiki along with other energy therapies. He documented significant improvement in kidney function evident in blood work—reduction of blood urea nitrogen (BUN) and also a reduction of blood glucose, which is exactly what Al has experienced. Article in *Massage and Bodywork Magazine* "Moving Energy Forward in the Scientific Realm," by Shirley Vanderbilt. Same results also printed in *Alternative Therapies* Mar/Apr 2003, Vol 9, #2.

"Reiki definitely helped my body cope with this condition. I think it keeps my blood more stable and my disease from advancing. It has helped me really relax. It was—still is— one the best mental and emotional supports I have experienced. It gave me the power to have a vision of continued health, especially when so many people painted a bleak picture for my condition.

Just before our session ended, Al turned to me and said, "I was right to take a stand against surgery. Now, I am convinced that my body and mind will tell me if and when I need a transplant. Until then, no surgery!"

May the Angels surround you, Al.

The Miraculous Human Spirit
When the Treatment Appears to Fail

I was anticipating the arrival of my next appointment. Casey was scheduled to be here any minute. She had called a few days before asking if I had done any work with infertility. "Yes," I responded. "I have worked with two women with long histories of infertility. Both conceived, had healthy pregnancies, and produced beautiful babies. I can't promise this will happen to you, but if you are willing to try, so am I." Casey explained that she had read about Reiki and had felt drawn to give it a try. She was tired and frustrated about her inability to become pregnant and needed to soothe body, mind, and spirit.

I have been an energy therapist for fifteen years now, and I believe in divine timing and intuitive messages. I felt that the succession of events leading Casey to my office was surrounded by positive signs. She heard encouraging conversations at work about Reiki, saw a special on TV about energy healing that really resonated with her, and finally found my brochure in a shop appropriately named "Angel Treasures." This prompted her to call me. After witnessing the happiness of two previously childless women and their "miracle babies," I felt reasonably optimistic about Casey and was anxious to begin working with her.

Just a few hours before Casey arrived, a bizarre incident occurred: I found a strange-looking card, the shape of a playing card, lying on my stairs. Apart from the fact that I keep my stairway neat, I had never seen it before and it did not belong to anyone in my house. Where did it come from? Baffled, I picked it up. On it was a picture of a dark-haired woman with a child sitting on her lap. *A woman with a child—did this picture hold any symbolic meaning for Casey?* I wondered.

Casey arrived at 2 P.M. sharp, just as we had planned. She was a pretty, dark- haired, young woman (just like on the card) with a bubbly personality. The intake interview went well; I found out a little more about Casey's medical history, and how she hoped to heal through Reiki. She had a very positive attitude in spite of her medical problems.

"I want to include a gentle healing modality in my life because the medical treatments for infertility I am undergoing are so hard on my body." She had been seeing a fertility specialist, one of the best in Michigan, for three years. She had had multiple tests done at the hospital to try to determine why she was not conceiving (no answers yet) and was on an extensive variety of pills and injections to increase her fertility. She had in-vitro fertilization a few months before but it failed.

I began our Reiki session by evaluating Casey's seven major chakras. Most of them were open, except for a block at her sacral chakra and her left ovary. She had been complaining of intermittent left-sided pain, which her doctor knew about but couldn't find the cause. I completed the session with the intention to unblock and balance Casey's energy system and provide her body with any additional energy to help it heal. I was confident universal energy would be drawn in by her body's natural intelligence and used exactly as it needed.

Casey decided to continue Reiki once a week for about a month. By the end of the first month, my intuition and previous signs convinced me that Casey would conceive naturally, perhaps even within the next month.

As the weeks went by, we changed our focus. Casey had decided to start preparing for her next in-vitro implant. Since she miscarried after the last one, she was especially concerned this time. I could see her anxiety building. I visually surrounded Casey with a protective pure white light and asked for a healthy pregnancy for her.

Time passed and Casey had the implant. She returned to my office a few weeks afterward. I had waited in anticipation for good news. Instead, she was very distraught.

"It didn't take!" she blurted out in between long, deep sobs muffled by her cradled hands. "I just had another miscarriage. My *baby* just died and I feel sick and emotionally exhausted."

I fell silent. I had also had a miscarriage in my past and could understand Casey's distress. Once pregnancy is confirmed, a woman usually forms a picture of a real child— how the child might look or act, and often dreams of names for this baby. The embryo becomes an actual person, even in this early stage.

Knowing that crying often helps to heal wounds and release tension, I offered a supportive space where Casey could let go of her grief. A short time later, she felt a little better, and began to share the true picture of her infertility.

She revealed her long and painful family history. For generations, women in her family, mother, many aunts, and cousins have been infertile or had great difficulty conceiving children for generations. "It took my mother years to have me." Casey looked at me through spread fingertips. "Honestly, are we cursed; is it karma? Why is this happening to me and my family?"

I observed her carefully. She was pale and bloated. *Chemically-altered* was written all over her face. I guessed there was too much toxicity in Casey's body. Her following statement confirmed my suspicion.

"I have been on oral Clomid several times in the past four years. It gave me tender breasts and made my body swell all over. I had hot flashes, stomach cramps, and sometimes dizziness. I also started a second drug, Pergonal, to prepare me for the surgery to remove some of my eggs for fertilization. I received painful Lupron injections, another hormone, once a day at home—my husband gave me the shots. I read that some of the drugs were new and poorly researched, which adds to my anxiety.

"In between all the drugs, I have had laparoscopes to see if I had any blockages in my ovaries or tubes, ultrasounds, hospital tests, lab work, and endless doctor appointments. Added to this physical torture is the financial burden of in-vitro fertilization at the hospital—$15,000 cash! Not including another $4,000 for drugs. And nothing is covered by insurance. After all this, I'm still not pregnant. My husband and I just want a child! We want to be parents like other couples. I'm thirty-two years old. It doesn't get easier as I get older."

The tears welled up in Casey's eyes again. "My husband and I have been on a grueling emotional roller-coaster ride. He sees me cry and can't help me. It tears him up inside and he cries too."

She thought for a moment, "I feel happy and hopeful one day and depressed and anxious another. Some days I can't get my *infertility* diagnosis out of my mind. It takes a huge effort to concentrate on something else. I have talked to other women at the fertility doctor's office. They feel that way, too.

"My periods are irregular and my hormones constantly shift and change in unnatural ways," she described further.

As she looked up at me, emotional pain was etched in her young face. "Infertility has a stigma; it is not talked of much in public. It's very personal. There is a sense of deep shame connected to it, as if there were something intimately flawed with you. As I hear about abused, unwanted children, I scream at the unfairness! Some women have children, and they don't even want them!" She buried her head in her hands again.

This time I understood Casey's condition better.

We completed our session in silence. Casey needed time to rest. In theory Reiki could improve energy and circulation in the pelvis, as well as help her body to detoxify. I made it my intention this would happen for Casey.

Before she left my office, she looked at me earnestly. "I don't know what else to do. I know this may sound crazy to women who conceive easily, but I'm saving for another in-vitro—$15,000. Maybe schedule a date in six months or so."

Casey reflected for a moment. "For now, I'm going to give my body a break and let my hormones balance out; focus on taking care of myself, and have Reiki a few times a month. Something positive has to come from all this!"

The humbling determination in her voice went straight to my heart. So much strength!

She added in a near whisper, "The other day, I mentioned a word to my husband I thought I would never say: *adoption*. Something we both might have to consider."

After the session, as she got into her car, Casey flashed me a brief smile before she drove away. "I'll be back next month!"

I admired her courage. So much to bear and yet to find the bravery to smile! I also felt a sense of sadness. I had been so sure of the success of Casey's last in-vitro. Did I see too much in dreams, messages, and medical intuition? Could they be wrong? Will Casey's dream of being a mother come true? I don't know. All I can do is offer Reiki.

Just when I thought the treatment had failed, there was a stunning turn of events: A month later Casey returned to my office. She was beaming. *"I'm pregnant!* I have morning sickness and I love it! So far it's a normal pregnancy.

"Sharon, I believe I became pregnant just days after our last Reiki session. It's miraculous to me and my husband! I want to thank you for being there to provide this much-needed therapy."

This time I felt that Casey's dreams of motherhood were about to come true through divine timing, divine intervention, and *a Reiki miracle*.

I spoke with Casey today. Her delivery date is rapidly approaching. Her pregnancy has progressed normally, and she and her husband couldn't be more elated.

The Surgery That Didn't Bleed

Judy looked up at the ceiling. Her whole body was tense. Despite pre-operative medication, beads of perspiration began to collect on her forehead and she was cold, clammy, and shaky. She was concerned about the outcome of today's surgery. A razor-sharp kidneystone was lodged firmly in her right ureter. She could no longer endure the constant pain that resided in her pelvis, and her doctors would *again* try to retrieve it. This surgery would be surgery number three. For some odd reason the stone was unwilling to be easily removed, and Judy had bled profusely during and after the previous two procedures. The doctor closed her up last time and sent her home without success.

Once in the hall, outside the operating room, Judy had little time to worry about today's outcome. *Besides, things would be different this time*, she thought. She had included Reiki to help balance and prepare her body for this invasion. Now, she was open to the possibility of more positive results.

Finally, the gurney lurched forward as the attendant pushed it toward the operating suite. They passed through the door, to suite #3, and Judy began to drift into a slightly altered state, the twilight zone. In just a moment the anesthesiologist would inject the epidural medication into her lower spine, infuse more Versed into the IV to sedate her, and she would be ready. Let the surgery begin!

Hours later, after the procedure was over, Judy became progressively oriented to a big surprise!

"Doctor, how did everything go? Did you get the stone out?"

He looked at her with a puzzled expression. "Everything went well and the stone is history, but frankly, I'm a little confused." He said. "Judy, you didn't bleed with this surgery—maybe there was a small amount, but nothing like before. The kidneystone was so easy to remove—I took it out in just minutes. Actually, unlike the past, it was a very short surgery! Did you do something different this time?"

Judy thought a while. *Yes, Doctor, I did something different. I'm going to tell you all about it at my first checkup in your office!*

She told me her story about two weeks after her discharge from the hospital. I greeted Judy at the door of my office. I couldn't help noticing her healthy glow. As she made herself comfortable on the table, she was eager to tell me all about her procedure.

"You know how frightened I was to have this surgery. The hemorrhaging I had last time was only one of my problems. I often faint right after surgery because my blood pressure drops quickly when I stand. My wounds don't generally heal fast and my pain threshold is low; I always need extra medication. But, with Reiki, things were different—I didn't have any of my usual problems. Boy, am I glad I included it!"

I helped prepare Judy for surgery by using a combination of Therapeutic Touch, Reiki, Hopi Indian techniques, and reflexology. I found total energy blocks in her sacral and solar plexus chakras. She felt powerless and frightened, blocking the solar plexus. The stone caused a physical block in the right side of her sacral chakra. I took such approaches as unruffling and smoothing her field, sweeping the heat off her right ureter, using an ancient Indian pain-drain method and filling the void with white light, using additional Reiki hand positions to her pelvic and kidney area, and applying pressure to reflex points on her feet to balance her field. I also provided distance healing and prayer the day of her surgery; its vibration can lay the matrix for physical healing.

After surgery, I gave Judy a traditional Reiki treatment. I combined it with polarity to balance the positive and negative poles of the body, yin and yang. Judy had some lingering back pain, which she said was relieved by that day's session. Her surgical site was completely healed by ten days post-op, and she quickly resumed daily activities.

After our final meeting, Judy assured me she does not look forward to having any more operations but sometimes it's a necessity. "I think of this one with gratitude and satisfaction...if such a thing exists—*this was a perfect surgery!*"

Studies

Observational and descriptive studies have indicated multiple benefits of Reiki, including pain reduction (Olson and Hansen, 1997), profound relaxation, and a sense of well-being (Chapman and Milton, 2002) *Massage and Bodywork Magazine* Feb/Mar 2004.

Wirth D.P., Richardson, J.T., Eidelman W.S., *Journal of Alternative and Complementary Medicine,* 1996, pp. 493–502. The Daniel Wirth study showed marked increase in wound healing with Therapeutic Touch.

Future research is needed to evaluate such occurrences in surgical procedures as reduced blood loss and post-surgical pain. We have just begun to explore these areas, *Spiritual Healing, A Scientific Validation of Healing Revolution,* by Daniel Benor, M.D., 2001.

Distance healing was found effective in enhancing recuperation from surgery in *"Effect of Distance Healing on Recovery from Surgery"* (Presentation at Second International Dead Sea Conference on the Anatomy of Well Being, Tiberius, Israel, 1993) *Spiritual Healing,* by Daniel Benor, M.D., 2001.

Waiting for Alicia

I looked into her tiny face. She was one of the prettiest babies I had ever seen. She had pink, rosy cheeks, clear blue eyes, and little blond ringlets nestled at the top of her head like a crown.

"Miracle baby! That's what she is," Julia said firmly as she sat on the couch next to me holding her new daughter. "We wouldn't have her without you, Sharon. With my infertility diagnosis and years of unsuccessful attempts, I had given up the idea of ever becoming a mother!"

As I sat next to her, the new mom looked radiant. She reported that the baby's entire eight-pound body was flawless!

"You can tell she's a *'Reiki Baby'*—she's not just healthy, she's peaceful and content, too." Julia told me with a satisfied expression.

"What's her name?" I asked with real interest.

"It's Alicia. It means *joy* in Hebrew. Her dad and I agree she has already brought us more joy than anything we've ever known. Her grandfather calls her *Little Angel* and admits he thought she'd never get here. I'm so glad you could come over today and see us before we went back home to Europe. We wanted to personally thank you for your part in helping us. My whole family is grateful."

"I'm pleased you made an appointment with me and were willing to try Reiki. So many people call out of curiosity and don't take any further action," I responded. "In my mind, most miracles are a team effort."

I fell silent for a few moments, as I watched Julia hug her precious bundle. I couldn't help thinking about the course of events that led to this miracle.

Julia's first Reiki appointment was less than a year ago. When we met, she told me that she and her husband were here from Austria working under a research grant. Julia explained she had previously been diagnosed with endometriosis, an abnormal condition of the uterus, and because of that was unable to become pregnant. She had been trying unsuccessfully for eight years and consequently experienced so much frustration.

Her best friend back home, a new Reiki Master, encouraged her to try some Reiki treatments while she was here in the States. After they talked, Julia did some research on her own and decided to call me right away for an appointment.

As she anxiously related her story, my attention was drawn to something so peculiar. Another woman had come to me for infertility over a year before—presently she was six months pregnant and doing well. Julia had *the exact same first name* as this other client, and even more peculiar, *their entire medical histories were nearly identical!* For a minute I felt like I was reliving a past experience. My intuition heightened. As a Master Teacher, my last *attunement* opened my brow chakra—increasing insight and sixth sense. With this gift, I was pretty sure I could help Julia have a healthy pregnancy, too.

The first Reiki session revealed an energy block in Julia's left ovary. It was similar to the other client. I focused on balancing the body's energy and paid close attention to her left side. My intention was to open this center and bring more healing energy into her pelvis. Sometimes blood circulation improves with energy treatments, which may bring more oxygen and nutrients to the reproductive organs. After the session she reported a lot of warming and tingling around her left ovary. I thought it was a good sign. I asked her to return in one week and she agreed.

Minutes after she left the office a powerful message came to me. I was still thinking about Julia. As I was putting a book back on a shelf, my deck of "healing with the angel" oracle cards (cards that offer positive and insightful messages), fell off and one spilled out in front of me. In bold letters I saw "**children**" on the face of the card. It quickly got my attention and I read its significance. It said: *New children may be coming into your life very soon.* I was taken aback, almost certain this message was for Julia.

Be patient and you will see, I thought.

Julia came for several more weeks. She told me she had previously made an appointment with an infertility specialist for an evaluation and information on in-vitro fertilization. She and her husband had some interest in trying it and were looking into the beginnings of this process. She promised to share the doctor's information with me.

Julia made an appointment for a session soon after seeing him. After she arrived we sat down in my office. I will never forget that moment. Her hands were visibly trembling. Her eyes were red from crying and she said she was anxious to tell me something. "Sharon, I had some routine blood work done when I saw the specialist. I still can't believe it! I'm two weeks pregnant!"

We were so excited! As we talked, we realized she became pregnant right after the third Reiki session!

"I know I should be elated about this," Julia said as she reached for another tissue. "Truth is, I'm happy but I'm really scared. I'm so afraid of having a miscarriage. I know that's common with endometriosis."

After I explained the benefits of Reiki during pregnancy, she decided to have a session once a week and see how things went.

"Reiki can be a real support for any medical condition," I continued. "I've just read a few articles from a newsletter from my national Reiki organization about the positive effects of Reiki for both pregnancy and delivery. They also said when mothers had Reiki during pregnancy, their babies were often more relaxed and less colicky."

"That's comforting," Julia said. "What else can Reiki do for me?"

"I believe it can help improve your body's natural immunity, balance reproductive energy, help you feel more relaxed, and provide emotional support during a very stressful time. During sessions I use the emotional healing technique to release old trauma from your reproductive system. I can also show you 'self-Reiki' techniques so you can reinforce our work at home. Finally, I use meditation and visualization exercises to help you 'see' yourself having a normal pregnancy, easy delivery, and healthy baby. Honestly, I'm sure it's a powerful ally to your obstetric care."

"I think I need *all* of that! I have been through so much

trauma and I want to give this baby the best chance possible," Julia assured me.

As the months passed, Julia continued to see me once every week or two. She was having a normal pregnancy in every way. She blossomed. No one was happier, and I was confident everything was going to be just fine.

The ninth month finally came. Plans for delivery at our local hospital had been made. At their request, I taught her husband some simple energy balancing techniques to ease Julia's labor in the hospital. I would help, too, by providing distance healing techniques after her admission.

When I got the call about labor, I opened the pathway to Julia with the Reiki distance healing symbol and "sent" Julia energy needed for delivery. I visualized Julia, her husband, and the new baby happy and healthy. I also said a brief prayer for Julia and her medical team. "God bless Julia's doctor and guide his hands during the delivery."

Julia called me right after she got home. She'd had an eight-hour labor, short for the first baby, and the delivery went very well. Her little family would be leaving for Austria early the following month and we had to say goodbye.

Well, here we are back to the beginning of the story. Remember, I'm visiting Julia and her new baby, Alicia—the one who brings *joy*. This is one of my most beloved stories. It still gives me tingles every time I talk about it…and yes, the card was right! My intuition was right on, too! I'm sure Reiki was a powerful intervention that helped prepare Julia for conception and have the best pregnancy she could ask for. Before I left their home, Julia mentioned something else.

"I had so much *energy* during my labor it surprised both me and my doctor," she beamed. Then she reflected, paused and suddenly, her face brightened, "Did Reiki do that?"

Scientific Study

Reiki is in the same family as acupuncture and can provide a similar effect. An acupuncture study, published in April 2002 in the medical journal *Fertility and Sterility,* found that *acupuncture increases the chance of pregnancy* for women undergoing in-vitro fertilization. A total of 160 women participated in the study. They were separated into two groups—one received acupuncture, one did not.

Twenty-one of the *untreated* women became pregnant and *thirty-four* of the *acupuncture-treated* women became pregnant—a significant improvement.

Report of Masked Randomized Trial

I always pray for my clients, especially those with infertility. I was pleased to find this information: A study by Cha, Wirth, and Lobo, New York Presbyterian Hospital and Columbia Center in New York City was done to determine if prayer can influence the success of in-vitro fertilization. 219 women were equally divided into two groups—one group prayed for, one not. Prayer groups were from the U.S., Canada, and Australia. Those prayed for were living in Seoul, Korea. Those prayed for had a higher pregnancy rate.

Successful implant—Prayed for—16.3%

Not prayed for—8%

Successful pregnancy—Prayed for—50%

Not prayed for—26%

Sexual Abuse
Healing from the Darkest Place

Maria was one of the most challenging clients I have ever encountered; the sexual abuse she experienced left multiple devastating effects on her entire being. Through the power of Reiki, she experienced a great deal of comfort, relief, and a "Reiki miracle." Maria symbolizes millions of people, throughout time, who have been sexually traumatized. So many remain silent but she chose to let the secret out. Because no one could tell it better, much of this story is told through the voice of Maria…

Maria and I met several years ago at a day of retreat for women. My impression was that she was a successful young woman both at home and in business. Maria seemed happy, healthy, and nearly carefree. She had a warm and friendly way of presenting herself, and during the first part of our friendship she mentioned only a few family problems. Her first Reiki appointment with me was a year after our original meeting.

We talked a few minutes before starting our first session. During that time, Maria disclosed a painful history of alcoholism in her immediate family. She had been dealing with those old issues again recently. Her focus today was to promote relaxation and improve her sleep pattern.

After she was comfortable on the table, I used the pendulum to evaluate her energy system. Her root, sacral, solar plexus, and throat chakras were fully closed. Her heart was excessively large, nearly wild, and her third eye and crown were perfectly open. Some ideas flashed into my mind before starting our session; they were hunches and gut feelings based on years of private practice.

Because her root was closed, I suspected Maria had, at some point, lacked basic needs in her life, and had possibly experienced unsafe conditions. Since her sacral chakra was closed, I felt a sexual conflict might be involved. A solar plexus closure meant personal power issues. The wild pattern of the heart center was one I had seen before, and can indicate confused sexual boundaries. A closed throat chakra could imply trouble with communicating and feeling verified.

With a beautifully open crown and brow chakra, I was certain Maria was intuitive, perceptive, and spiritually connected. From our previous conversations, I knew this to be true; she had great faith in God, which gave her strength for survival on the earth plane.

As I balanced her energy in Reiki tradition, we completed the treatment in silence.

After the session, Maria began to collect her things and prepared to leave. As we exchanged conversation, I couldn't seem to shake the foreboding sense of sadness I had experienced while working in her field.

"Is there anything you'd like to talk about before you go?" I asked her.

There was a long pause. "I'm not ready," she replied as she turned her eyes away from me.

Maria made another appointment and returned in a few weeks. That day, she could no longer remain silent. "I'm coming for Reiki to help free myself from a dark past. I see Reiki as a support, especially to my psychotherapy."

Maria went on to explain, "I'm a victim of sexual abuse, and I have struggled with it for years. My psychologist told me I was not alone, that as many as twenty-five percent or more of all American women have experienced some kind of sexual abuse in their lives."

"I'm a caring listener," I assured her, "Continue if you are comfortable."

Maria nodded and then began her story. "When I was three, incest began right in my own home. Adding to the pain, when I was four, the family priest sexually traumatized me."

She recalled the day with tears running down her cheeks. "My entire family was home one Friday. We were expecting a visit from our parish priest. The priest was taking my brother away on a weekend trip to church camp. Church camp was more of an obligation than fun. Right after his arrival, a tornado-like storm suddenly blew in. We all, Father included, went to the basement for shelter. Right after we went downstairs, we lost power and all the lights went out. We stayed down there in the dark while the storm raged. I was afraid and began to cry. Our priest picked me up and held me tightly in his arms to help me feel more secure, but instead, I felt uneasy for reasons I couldn't explain. After the storm passed, my family made their way back upstairs. The priest however, held me back for a few minutes, and we lingered in the dark basement. I was alone with him. He held me close and wouldn't let me go. I could feel his breath on my neck. His hands began to roam around my tiny body, go under my panties, and in places I instinctively knew were forbidden. It felt wrong, very wrong, and it terrified me. Although I was alone with the priest only a few minutes, it seemed like an eternity before he carried me upstairs. My whole body shook and went numb. I opened my mouth to scream, but not a sound came out. The silent scream I held inside would fester and torment me for years to come."

"Why didn't you tell your parents?" I asked, with so much compassion for Maria.

"For one thing," Maria continued, "it's very difficult for a four-year-old to explain that sort of thing. Also, back then, priests were seen as 'near Gods' in my family and also by much of the Catholic community. No one in my family ever challenged the behavior of priests; it was a sin to do so. With him being seen as sacred by my parents, I suffered even greater emotional wounds through his unethical actions. That incident still haunts me today."

She paused for a few moments to gather her thoughts.

"I endured about fourteen years of incest at home by a close relative. Sometimes the abuse would happen even during family gatherings in a barn or outbuilding.

"I came from a large family of thirteen children. My parents tried to maintain an image of a perfect family. Ignorance and poverty added to our dysfunctional picture.

"I tried to tell my mother many times about the incest, but she beat me for 'telling lies.' There were times my mother looked at me as if she believed me, but ultimately she turned on me with a vengeance, 'It's all your fault. You cause your own problems!'"

Maria recalls an especially painful time, "One day when I was about ten, I was washing up after an unwanted sex act. In a daze, I let the water run too long into the bathtub. The well at home was shallow, and went dry. I was accused of running it dry on purpose and got a whipping for it.

"My teen years were unbearable. I remember having severe pain from gallstones. I sought treatment and was punished. Seeing a doctor was too costly for a poor family; it was a luxury, not a necessity."

Maria went on to say that as a confused young teen, with a dysfunctional sexual history, she became promiscuous and had an early pregnancy. She was alone with no support and unequipped to care for a baby. Complicating the situation, gallbladder disease was escalating, and the pain from it was so great she started fainting in school. Finally, a date was set to have her gallbladder removed. In those days doctors refused to perform that kind of surgery while pregnant, and the procedure was now urgent.

"I chose to have an abortion without the knowledge of my parents; I was sure they would beat me for becoming pregnant. The decision was agonizing for me and intensified by secrets and guilt.

"My motto became don't talk, don't feel, don't trust. I sank into a world of darkness, and my childhood memories were deeply buried until I was thirty. I hadn't even told my husband everything. I was too ashamed and afraid of rejection. Then, uncontrolled memories surfaced in the form of flashbacks called *post traumatic stress disorder*. I suffered just as much as people who had survived a terrible war."

After this revealing conversation, Maria thanked me for listening. She said, "I'm so glad I'm coming for Reiki today. It completely relaxes my body and helps me cope with the anxiety from flashbacks. As I told you, human touch has been a painful and frightening part of my past. Since there is very little touch involved in Reiki treatments, I feel particularly safe with this type of therapy."

At the closing of this session, I was glad I could help Maria in any way possible. I was also reminded of man's inhumanity to man; sadly, behavior that has persisted far too long on this planet.

Total silence. I hadn't heard from Maria for many months. Then she called for an appointment.

"I really need a Reiki session soon. I'm exhausted from a long hospital stay. I'll tell you more later."

"I was concerned about you," I said when she arrived, "What happened?"

"I had a total hysterectomy last fall; consequently my hormones were out of whack and afterward I sank into a severe depression. With the 'force of a tornado,' the face of the priest returned to haunt me, old memories surfaced, and all the emotions of terror and shame erupted again. When I had thoughts of suicide, I knew I needed professional help, and I was immediately admitted to the hospital."

A full team of doctors worked for weeks to put Maria back together again. They felt that Maria's attitude and her past willingness to seek healing through self-help, psychotherapy, and other holistic healing modalities contributed to a more rapid recovery than the average person. She was an inspirational patient. She was placed on a new hormone routine and antidepressant medications. She continued to see her therapist, and called me for more Reiki sessions.

While Maria remained silent about her past abuse, *her physical body spoke.* Her medical team decided she had many illnesses related to emotional factors with stress and abuse at the core, such as: irritable bowel, gallstones, psoriasis, dense pelvic scar tissue, diabetes, multiple allergies, chronic anxiety, and finally, major depression. Their advice was to continue to find support she could trust and let all the secrets out.

I continued to be an empathetic listener, balance her energy field, and offered her *sacred space* as our sessions continued.

"With all that's happened in your life, how has Reiki helped you?" I asked, eager to know what role my chosen healing modality played in her recovery.

"It was a great comfort to me. It helped me release some of my heavy burdens, especially with forgiveness issues, which on many days were overwhelming to deal with. During Reiki sessions I safely connected with my past, and let go of abuse a little bit at a time. I felt both safety and trust, which was so often violated in my life. There were times I felt angry and you supported me as I expressed myself. You assured me I was *a strong survivor*, and I needed that. I am still healing from all the recent pelvic surgery. I had a reduction in pain and rapid improvement in the redness and swelling in my incision after our last session. I also went into remission from psoriasis, the irritating skin condition I had for twenty years. I am so relieved not to have all the itching and dryness on my hands and scalp. No medication ever healed it. I relaxed more deeply and slept better. One day, you cleared my spiritual field.[7] It was perfect and helped me feel more connected to God. I know Reiki is not faith healing, but all these positive effects are *miraculous* to me."

Just two days after our last session, I got a phone call from Maria. She told me she felt *Reiki energy* had provided grounds for another "miracle" to take place. For the first time in her life, one of her abusers acknowledged what he had done, and apologized for his actions that took place thirty years ago. "I never expected that. His confession verified my memories, which are another step toward emotional closure."

Despite Maria's horrific past, she is moving full steam ahead toward complete wellness. We continue with our Reiki sessions as Maria wishes, and with each one she takes another step toward being whole.

After she gave me permission to write her story she said, "Please use my real name in your book; it will be part of my healing."

As a Reiki Master, my understanding of how sexual abuse affects the mind, body, and spirit expanded through working with Maria, my teacher.

I would like to take this time to honor her for this candid interview. She is inspirational to me. I salute her strength, her courage, her willingness to speak out through written testament, and her perseverance in this most difficult healing journey.

As I wrote Maria's story, it seemed as if I was a channel for an endless chorus of voices...emerging from the beginning of time...*who have never been heard.*

Namaste, I bow my head to you, Maria, and may God bless you.

---

[7] I cleared and balanced Maria's spiritual field by placing my right hand on her abdomen and my left one on her forehead. This position is calming and promotes spiritual equilibrium, helping those who have experienced stress and shock.

Closing Comment

I revealed more of this client's past, because this urgent issue is not talked about enough. No longer surprising, about forty percent of the women who come to me for Reiki have a buried, abusive past. It is *protectively encapsulated* and hiding at the core of their chest pain, depression, arthritis, chronic infections, and a gamut of other diseases. The face of perpetrators varies greatly, but the destructive evidence left behind is the same. The *core* often goes unrecognized by general medicine. Most of my clients have said they do not talk to their medical doctors about these issues—no time and far too personal to discuss in a busy, hurried office. I have found that when the client expresses herself, is verified and supported in a compassionate manner, and continues with Reiki, the medical condition improves.

Karen's Way

This story is a "memorial" to honor Karen, a long-term cancer survivor, friend, and fellow Reiki Master. As a former oncology nurse, I was so impressed by her—I had never seen anyone with advanced cancer look so healthy or live as long as Karen did. She testified that Reiki was one of the most valuable tools she had to help her cope with her grim diagnosis. Karen demonstrated the power of both receiving treatments and applying it to herself, called self-Reiki. She included a daily dose of this therapy, which acted as a synergist. Reiki strengthened the effects of her traditional and alternative methods, and that, in my eyes, produced the formula for a miracle.

The doctor stood in silence at the bedside. He lowered his head for a moment and prepared himself for the sobering conversation he would have with the patient's husband, pacing in the hospital waiting room just around the corner. He had never met anyone like Karen in his entire practice, and perhaps he never would again. He had really tried to take his traditional medical stand with her during their doctor-patient relationship. But somewhere along the way, Karen had shaken his Western way of thinking—forming a significant crack in the solid framework of his fine medical education, just by being herself. He had not suspected that God had formally assigned Karen to planet Earth to carry out an *alternative* teaching mission, and she had completely fulfilled her contract in a very short time.

Dr. Young immediately recognized Karen's husband when he entered the private waiting room. "I'm sorry, Steve, I'm afraid Karen may have only twenty-four hours or less to live. She's entered the last stages, and there's nothing more I can do for her." He put his hand on Steve's shoulder and gave it a firm squeeze. "You know the prognosis, it's inevitable."

"I'm not really supposed to get that close to my patients, it's not seen as professional, but I have known Karen so long now, and I have a great deal of respect for her. Honestly, I feel like I'm losing my own sister. I'm so sorry." These were the last words from the oncologist as he prepared to emerge into the blackness of the night.

Karen was heavily medicated and had slipped into a semi-coma a few days earlier. Her friends provided both distance Reiki and actual treatments at the hospital to help Karen with her transition. Near the end, they noticed Karen's energy gathered up and remained concentrated around her head and crown, a typical pattern at the end of life.

Her passing was gentle; she was ready. The native drums called, and she easily followed them into the realm beyond.

I am introducing you to Karen, someone who astounded everyone she met, especially her doctors. She was diagnosed with aggressive breast cancer with lymph node infiltration fourteen years ago. Steve, Karen's husband and soulmate, reports that after her mastectomy, Karen had five cancer-free years. Everyone thought she was cured.

Then almost to the day of her fifth cancer-free "anniversary," her stomach began to bother her. She was fully examined, scanned, and subjected to mountains of lab work. Her immediate diagnosis was metastatic cancer of the lungs, spine, and multiple other invaded sites. Her medical picture was grave: six months to a year, at best, to live. It was a severe shock and an overwhelming challenge. Karen was extremely frightened. But faith and unseen forces would help her survive, even thrive.

She immediately received traditional treatment, chemotherapy, once a week to once a month. Often her chemo was the most aggressive or the newest on the market—state-of-the-art and best available. After the first year, Karen tolerated the treatments with minimal side effects, and lived far better than anyone expected. Two years passed, then three, four, and five. Karen remained alive and well!

I met her six years after her "fatal" prognosis. She looked vibrant, with a healthy glow. We first met at a friend's home to participate in a Reiki exchange—we were both Reiki Masters. She mentioned she was getting cancer treatments and Reiki was very helpful to her. As I provided this therapy for Karen, I noticed her energy field had unusual qualities for someone on chemo. She was open and balanced, and her energy had a fine and soothing vibration—I asked her how she did that.

"I give myself Reiki treatments," she said. "I place my hands on my own chakras just ten minutes a day, starting with my head and ending at my feet. I also use the distance symbol and transfer energy into my future, especially on chemo days. It's an easy way to keep my body's energy in balance. I see it like taking a shot of vitality—a once a day boost of 'chi.' When I teach Reiki, I recommend self-Reiki for any illness or just to keep the body in harmony."

Karen said she used many other alternative approaches as well. "Even my doctor is pleased with the results!"

One day we had an opportunity to talk at length. "Tell me more, what else do you do to keep yourself well? I'm really interested."

It seemed Karen was waiting for this opportunity to speak, and she had plenty to say. "About a year after I was first diagnosed, I began to search for an alternative healing program; conventional methods alone were not enough for me. Looking for new treatment methods began as a leap of faith. I knew something was out there and began my quest. The first thing I had to do was to adopt a positive attitude. I read that negative thoughts and fears neutralize the powerful forces that bring about healing. Chemicals produced by *feelings of fear* are the most devastating to our bodies, producing fertile grounds for cancer cells to grow. I surrounded myself with positive and inspirational people— those who supported and uplifted me in my quest. I took many classes, read, and did a lot of research. I began to do community work in Michigan through the American Cancer Society's 'Reach for Recovery' program and shared my story by speaking to local groups.

"I became extremely interested in energy healing. First, I took classes in Therapeutic Touch, and then went on to take Reiki to the Master Level. There were a few benefits I noticed right away as I began to practice Reiki—I felt closer to God as I gave treatments and I also experienced healing in myself as I was healing others. Growing passion inspired me to take more—polarity and craniosacral classes, too.

"Next, I began visualizing exercises daily. I 'see' myself as well and happy. I have learned to love, honor, and be content with myself, just the way I am. I do not have to be perfect to be loved. That has not been easy. I give myself permission to do things I have always wanted to do. I go on a vacation from my obsessive planning and find a place to celebrate life and the people I love. Whenever possible I take a real vacation or mini-trip.

"I pray every day, asking for divine guidance, and when I meditate, I receive God's answers. It's not good to stay 'up in my head' (meditating or thinking deeply) all the time so I ground myself whenever I can by taking a long walk—connecting back to the energy of mother earth. These are simple but powerful things."

"I know your routine is multifaceted. What about the foods you eat and herbal remedies?" I inquired.

"As often as possible, I eliminate the caffeine routine and eat low-fat and low- sugar. I don't eat red meat and processed foods, just fresh produce. I also take a digestive enzyme like papaya right after my meals to help absorb nutrients better.

"Detoxification is extremely important after getting chemo. It is one of the most important things I do. I start as soon as I arrive home after chemo, and I experience fewer side effects. Chemo should not stay in your system; it's too potent. It destroys not only bad cells but the good ones as well. To help flush it out, I drink lots of water, alternating distilled water with regular water to reduce ingesting harsh minerals. I substitute regular tea with detoxifying tea for three days straight. Make a pot and sip it all day. I may experience some gas or a headache, but this is natural as I begin my internal cleansing process. Sometimes, I change teas and drink a cup or two of dandelion or parsley tea. I also drink green tea; it's a powerful antioxidant that helps increase the compounds that destroy cancer cells."

"Karen, you are so active. How else do you keep your energy level up?"

"To people on chemo I say *keep your energy level up with protein drinks*; they supply you with amino acids to rebuild the body and allow the immune system to stay strong.

"I also take a complete multivitamin with minerals every day and use fasting, juicing, colon cleansing (colonics), enemas, etc., found in the book *Prescription For Nutritional Healing,* by James and Phyllis Balch. With colonics, see a specialist for this; it isn't to be done alone. Chemo toxin reabsorbs in the bowel and gets right back into the blood, thus adding to its side effects—so move chemo on through A.S.A.P." Karen paused to take a breath.

"I just thought of something else that helps me. My massage therapist uses a technique called 'Lymphatic Draining.' It's detoxifying for the lymph system. I see my lymphatic system as the 'National Guard' of my immunity. It delivers nutrients, oxygen, and hormones to the tissues, and takes waste away. Another thing to help this, I use Pau D'Arco and Hanna Kroeger's Lymph Tea.

"My last method for detoxifying is participation in the ancient Native American sweat lodge. I actually created one right in my own yard. It is not only physically cleansing but spiritually expanding as well. Another more simple method to induce a sweat is through aerobic exercise."

"Gee, Karen, you really have an interesting approach. Have any other advice?"

"I sure do. Finally, and most importantly, take the time

to find a doctor who supports you and your beliefs. Not just for cancer, but for all your medical challenges. Good bedside manners, clear communication, and simple kindness go a long way. Find someone you are comfortable with. And, yes, tell your doctor any alternative/ complementary methods you are using. I told my doctor everything. I said I was following his treatment plan, but I was doing it my way, too. I wouldn't be Karen if I didn't. His response was, 'You're doing great; keep on doing it.' He has become sincerely interested in my whole routine, even Reiki. In fact he wants a copy of my survival plan to share with his other patients who are interested. I thought I saw him taking notes last time we talked! I'm so proud of him. He's really coming around!" Karen told me with her impish grin.

"What about your family? Do they support your beliefs?" I asked as I repositioned myself in the easy chair across from Karen.

"At first, my husband didn't believe in Reiki or any of the other methods I used. But he changed his mind after the first year and shows a lot of interest now. I give him a Reiki treatment whenever he asks for one. Many of my relatives have taken my Reiki classes, even my young nieces and nephews. Through my classes, they now have a gift for life; they know how to help themselves and others heal. We are all natural born healers—we just need a little direction. Passing on this sacred information has made me feel so good!"

As her husband confirmed, "Karen did love to talk!" She often said, "Many people wait for grand and impressive opportunities to do good things, when the very condition they require is found in the simplest and most familiar places."

The last time I saw Karen, she was in her "simple" surroundings, doing "good" things. She was in the local grocery store, hairless from the chemo, smiling, and giving encouragement to customers, especially anyone who had been ill. Sometimes she connected with someone else who was getting chemo. She was kind to everyone despite her own personal challenges. Karen never seemed to find the time to complain.

We do not understand why many things happen, especially when loved ones are taken away "too soon." Sadly, after a total of fourteen years of responding to the planet's most sophisticated treatments, Karen ultimately began to lose ground. She experienced extreme weakness, became a shadow of her former self, and finally succumbed to physical illness. Even then, she continued to be Karen and did things her way.

The Native American ceremony brought ancient practice to the modern funeral home where Karen was placed to rest. Karen had chosen an alternative method of memorial. Her extraordinary service was conducted by a fourth generation descendent of the much respected Mohawk chief, "Thayendanegea" (also called Chief Joseph Brant). This decedent's title is "pipe carrier." He is appointed to carry this special pipe for sacred ceremonies by his native community because he leads an honorable life, treats his family well, and is a respected role model for the young. He is also very spiritual, and is the chosen one to pray for the sick or anyone else who needs prayers.

To begin the service, the Mohawk man and his wife, a wise woman who was tenderly assisting him, lit sage bundles to begin the smudging process. The beautiful smoky aroma of the north woods permeated into all the nooks and crannies of Karen's imaginary lodge. Through smudging, Karen and her surroundings would be purified, protected, and freed of negative energies. Amidst the smoke, the pipe carrier approached Karen and spoke to her as if she were still alive. He gave her advice and encouragement to meet all the challenges that were soon coming to her.

According to native custom, her spirit would begin a year-long journey, remaining close to the earth plane. During this time she would relearn anything she needed to, correct any wrongdoings, and gather beloved items for her spiritual pilgrimage ahead. She may stop to visit many friends and relatives during this time. Occasionally, a few of her most valued items or trinkets may turn up missing from her former home. Possibly, someone there would get a fleeting glimpse of her, or perhaps she would remain unseen. If they showed fear, she would not visit them again. The Native philosophy says that when loved ones release the deceased and do not continue to grieve and hold on, it is much easier for the spirit to go to the next world.

At the end of the pipe carrier's conversation, the native couple prepared to address the four directions of the world—east, south, west, and north, turning in a full circle. Each direction represents certain qualities, colors, or energies. Circles are an important part of the Indian philosophy and hold meaning even at the end of life. As they spoke I recalled one of my favorite native songs, "Everything an Indian does is in a circle: birth, youth, old age, death, and reincarnation, where birth begins again. Death is not the end; it is merely a new beginning. Everything we see that is powerful moves in a circle; the sun and moon are round and move in circles. The wind in its greatest power whirls in a circle."

The prayer energy from Karen's friends and family was transferred into the tobacco, which was placed into the sacred pipe. The pipe was filled, held upward, and offered to the "spirit keepers." Spirit keepers are like angels or wise men; they guide us and teach us how to live.

Finally, the time came to address these directions. First, the ceremonial leader turned to the east where the sun rises, symbolized by the color red, where tobacco is the sacred gift, and offered his pipe to the spirit keepers.

He turned to the south where it is warmed by the sun, the color is yellow, the gift is cedar, and offered his pipe to the spirit keepers.

He turned to the west where the sun sets, the color is black, the gift is sage, and offered his pipe to the spirit keepers.

He turned to the north where it is cold, the color is white, the gift is sweet grass, and offered his pipe to the spirit keepers.

The circle had been completed.

Rejoining his wife, they ended with silence and prayer to God, the Great Mystery, creator of all people and all things.

After closing the service, the loved ones departed. The Mohawk remained behind to smoke his pipe with Karen, releasing her spirit and urging her to begin her sacred journey.

The nontraditional approach was beautifully captivating, and it was *so* Karen. Again, as a teacher, she taught us something we would never forget. As a Reiki Master, she reached a high level of spiritual maturity and demonstrated that she was the master of her own life.

As I sat quietly, surrounded by memories of Karen, I saw wisdom, love, respect, bravery, honesty, humility, and truth—the "Seven Teachings of the Grandfathers." It's what we all should have. Moments passed as I reflected in silence. Then came the whisper of a very soft voice, *"Let the journey begin, Aho."*

Wakan Tanka nici un (May the Great Spirit guide you).

Study on Cancer and Energy Healing

In a study by Chen Guoguang, cancers were present in fourteen different parts of the body for twenty-four people. Duration of treatment lasted from eight months to twelve years. After Qigong energy healing (similar to Reiki), noticeable improvements occurred in twenty-nine percent of those in the study. Improvements included decreased pain, reduced swelling, disappearance of blood in stool, improved appetite, better sleep, and many others. Reported at Second International Conference on Qigong-Xian, China-Sept 1989. published in *"Spiritual Healing,"* by Daniel Benor, M.D., 2001, p. 397.

Books Karen recommended

Prescription for Nutritional Healing, 1997, by James Balch, M.D., and Phyllis Balch, C.N.C.

All Women Are Healers, 1990, by Diane Stein

The Edgar Cayce Handbook for Health through Drugless Therapy, 1996, by Harold Reilly and Ruth Brod

Options, the Alternative Cancer Therapy Book, 1992, by Richard Walters

Spirit Healing, 1991, by Mary Dean Atwood

Empowerment through Reiki, 1998, by Paula Horan

Conversations with God, 1996, by Neale David Walsh

Animal-Speak, 1993, by Ted Andrews

Healing Animals

Animals are one of the greatest gifts to mankind. Their contributions are most obvious when, as pets, they provide unconditional love, companionship, protection, and help us heal just by being present. They easily experience our stresses and take on part of our emotional pain, thus often contracting the very same diseases their owners have. I recall that my mother-in-law's poodle went into congestive heart failure at the exact same time she did. Both were prescribed nearly identical medication and lived an equal amount of time. Since animals provide so much emotional or physical healing for us, it is only natural we want to return this kindness to them.

When it comes to energy therapies, animals differ from humans in that *they do not have preconceived ideas* about the treatment. They have no prejudice or fear, welcome it unconditionally, and readily allow healing to occur. I find it to be true when I work with them. A sick animal will come to me instinctively and usually exposes the body part that needs to be worked on.

Humans and animals share similar chakras and meridians and are positively affected through energy-balancing techniques. When giving an animal a treatment, I begin at the head and finish by grounding at the feet. Because of their smaller size and sensitivity, their session is just five to fifteen minutes. The animals usually get up or walk away when they have had enough.

Energy therapies can help with pain relief, stimulate wound healing, relieve emotional distress, and provide stability with chronic diseases for pets, too. I think our "best friends" deserve it!

Just Homesick

My friend Lauren moved into a new home in my neighborhood. I was anxious to stop in and welcome her. That afternoon, when I arrived, she gave me the "grand tour" and then we sat down in the dining room for coffee. As we were talking, her dog, Cindy, sauntered in and lay down on the floor next to me.

As Lauren looked down, her expression quickly dimmed. "Oh, Sharon, I'm worried about Cindy. She's not been herself since we moved in a few days ago. She doesn't eat or drink and hasn't gone to the bathroom since yesterday evening. I'll take her to the vet if she doesn't improve within a few hours. I'm curious, what do you think is going on?"

I leaned over to Cindy and put my hands on her furry body. An extreme sadness overcame me as I got in touch with her energy. A few pictures came into my mind.

"Lauren, I get the feeling your dog is grieving. She is missing her old home. Dogs use images to transmit their feelings and Cindy is sending me a powerful picture of *homesickness.* The only home she ever knew is the one you just left and she wants to go back."

"Not on your life! This is home now and we're staying! Is there anything you can do? Can you give her one of your *magic treatments?*" Lauren asked with a little smirk.

I gently slid off the chair and sat down on the floor next to Cindy. I centered myself for a moment and placed my hands briefly around her head. I quickly proceeded on to her heart charka—that's where the real trouble was. I used the Reiki emotional healing symbol there, to release the trauma of the new move, and silently communicated with her. "Cindy, it's not possible to go back. This is your home now and you can be happy here. Besides, your owners care about you and need you to protect them just like you did before." I grounded her by gently holding her feet, and then spent a few extra minutes lavishing attention on her. She licked my hand and appeared less tense when I was finished.

"Well, Lauren, I've got to go now." I said, as I reached into the closet and got my coat. "I really hope your dog improves. I know how much she means to you."

The next morning I got a phone call from Lauren. "Hey, *your magic touch worked!* As soon as you left, Cindy went over to her dish and ate all her food. Then she got a big drink, and went outside for a bathroom break. That was amazing! She's just fine today. By the way, thanks, you saved us more worry and a big vet bill, too!"

I have walked past my friend's house many times. Each time, I see Cindy fiercely guarding her new home... As if she has lived there a lifetime!

Bright Eyes

I took a long look at my cat, Sunny. Something didn't seem right. Then I noticed that his left eye was red and had started to weep. He kept pawing at it. He didn't seem to be in pain, just annoyed with his condition. *Allergies,* I thought. *It's ragweed season. Even animals can react to it.*

I washed his eye out with cool water before he headed out doors for his usual adventures.

That night when he returned, Sunny looked worse; his left eye was beginning to swell and redden even more. I was concerned. By morning it looked really infected—hot, swollen, and had a thick, odorous discharge. Even the tissue around his eye was inflamed. Sunny looked at me as if he were pleading for help.

It nearly broke my heart to see him that way; he was such a gentle cat and had been part of our family for several years. I remembered the first time I met Sunny. He was an abandoned kitten surviving alone in the woods near my home. He came into our lives looking for food and people to care for him. We adopted him and had a special bond since then.

I made an urgent vet appointment and took him in right away. After Dr. Cook examined Sunny, he had a perplexed look on his face.

"I can't see any reason for such a rapid onset of this infection. I'll start antibiotics right now and give him eye drops, too. See you back in a week for a recheck. Call me if it gets any worse. There's a strange black spot I can't identify in the center of his iris. Most unusual!"

As soon as we returned home, I let my cat rest for awhile. He seemed tired and irritable. As he tried to clean his eye, he quickly jerked his head back at the slightest touch from his paw. Poor Sunny looked so miserable!

I was hopeful Therapeutic Touch could help him find some relief and pulled Sunny onto my lap. As I began to work on him, I noticed a lot of heat in the field around his eye. I swept the heat away with my right hand. Then I unruffled this energy by making short, sweeping strokes over his entire body to free congestion and stimulate energy flow. Finally, I smoothed his field by making long, slow strokes from his head down to his paws. Last, I grounded him by massaging his paws, one by one for a few minutes. He relaxed a bit and rolled onto his back to let me work on his belly, too. I was touched by his trust in me. I thanked Sunny for allowing me to work with him.

Because he was a small cat, I spent only ten minutes doing Sunny's treatment. He instinctively cooperated fully with my therapy. Animals openly welcome and even seek these healing hands when they are ill. They have no judgment or preconceived ideas. I repeated the treatment three times a day for the rest of the week, always with Sunny's cooperation. At times he requested a session in his own particular way. He lifted his head up close to my hands to make sure I worked over his sore eye. And then, as cats do, he got up and walked away when he'd had enough.

Sunny began to respond to his medical and complementary care by the third day. He looked much better, the discharge and heat had gone and he quit rubbing his eyes. Only the strange black spot remained. In fact it was even more prominent.

When we returned, Dr. Cook was surprised to see him looking so good.

"I don't believe it!" he said, puzzled, as he reexamined

Sunny. "I think my question has just been answered. Now I know what that strange black spot is. He's got a large thorn embedded in his eye! I'll have to remove it right away, and then keep him overnight for observation," the doctor informed me. Then he scratched his head as he remarked, "With a foreign body in his eye how did it heal so completely?"

"I'm not surprised," I said, "I have done Therapeutic Touch several times a day while continuing his antibiotics. Have you ever heard of this therapy?"

"Why, yes. I just saw a video on a satellite channel about energy healing for animals. It was so interesting. Now that you mention it, I can clearly see that your cat has benefited. Tell me a little more about this technique."

After we talked, Dr. Cook confided he had been worried about Sunny. "I was afraid he might lose his sight or worse yet, that I'd have to remove his eye."

He made a full recovery soon after this procedure. The vet saved the thorn for me. It was nearly a half inch long and came from a particular bush that grows in our swamp.

As we drove home from this ordeal, I looked affectionately over at Sunny. I have heard people say they love their animals almost as much as their children. As I embraced that idea, I was certain the value of this therapy cannot be estimated in dollars. It is priceless!

Scientific Study

Canadian experimenter Bernard Grad did a pilot study on 300 mice with identical surgical incisions on their backs. Healer Oscar Estebany held his hands over a controlled group for two fifteen-minute sessions for sixteen days. These mice healed more quickly than usual. The most useful part—*mice do not respond to suggestion, therefore the placebo effect had nothing to do with rapid recovery.*[8]

---

[8] *Journal of the American Society for Psychical Research*, 1965, p. 100.

Distance Healing

Many studies have been done that show patients who receive a variety of prayer and distance healing techniques heal much faster and with fewer complications that those who do not. I often add Reiki distance healing techniques to my clients' "prayer pool" to increase their chances for greater results.

Dr. Krucoff, at the prestigious Duke University Medical Center, participated in a study to see how prayer and distance healing methods affect procedures for cardiac patients undergoing angioplasty and artery dilation. The Krucoff team looked at what happened when a huge variety of denominations—Christians (Catholics and Protestants), Silent Unity, Jews, and Buddhists—prayed for a random fifty percent of the uninformed patients. The thirty patients being prayed for tolerated cardiac procedures 50-100% better than those not prayed for. The study is being expanded and was a focus of national attention reported in *Time* magazine, October 12, 1998. A similar study is ongoing at Harvard— just the fact that distance-healing is being studied at Harvard Medical School speaks volumes!

I often use distance healing as described in the next story.

Going the Distance for Dan

I looked at my dining-room clock. The timing was right on. My friend Dan should be heading into the hospital surgical suite at this very moment for an extremely rare operation. The challenge was huge for everyone involved—for Dan, his medical team, and his family.

I became centered in my quiet, wooded setting. Next, in Reiki fashion, I drew the ancient distance healing symbol and opened the pathway to him.

I moved through the pathway mentally and in seconds reached Dan. I imagined his physical form, just became a quiet observer, and then applied the sacred healing symbols to his entire body to help him emotionally, physically, and spiritually.

In my mind's eye, I saw the surgery going well. I visualized him pain-free and beginning to mend right after the very last suture was put in place. I lingered in those positive thoughts for a short time. I mentally asked the universe to repeat the treatment as many times as needed for the following week and "set the timer" for that to happen.[9]

Finally, I envisioned Dan completely well and enjoying life to the fullest. I was grateful for all the rapid recovery he would experience and placed him in the hand of the higher power until we could meet again.

My meditative state came to a close. Dan's distance healing was complete and I returned to my day.

Shortly after that session, my thoughts kept returning to him. I was really concerned. Worry is natural, but it's negative energy. I consciously made an extra effort to replace it with positive feelings.

Dan had come to my office for an "emergency session" two days before. He had just found out he had a rare and aggressive cancer in his nose, sinus cavity, and part of his facial bones. He was instantly scheduled for surgery at one of the country's most prestigious hospitals. A large section of his mid-face, including his nose, would be removed immediately! Everything happened so quickly; he had little time to think deeply about any of this. Just do it; no choice! After our first session Dan agreed and welcomed distance healing to be added to his regimen.

Time passed. A week later, the doorbell rang. It was my friend; he had come for a postsurgical Reiki treatment. A large pressure dressing was snugly wrapped around the middle of his face. He looked weak and still shaken, but stable.

"Hey, it's good to see you! I thought about you all week. How did the surgery go?"

Dan sat down and collected himself. "I have something good to tell you." He paused. "It was very successful and the doctor says I'm cancer free now. He was able to remove all of it. I don't need chemo, just radiation!"

I sighed with relief and sat down next to Dan. "And what did you think of distance healing? Did you feel or notice anything unusual?" I asked with anticipation.

Dan's face brightened. "Unusual? Sharon, get this, I had *no pain* after surgery. I didn't take any narcotic medication that was ordered for me at the hospital. Every time the nurse asked me if I wanted something for pain, I said, 'No thank you, I don't have any pain.'"

"'Are you sure?' she asked, surprise in her voice. 'So many facial nerves have been cut and my other patients require strong medication to cope with the pain.'

"Days later, when the doctor removed my dressing, he

couldn't believe how much my wound had healed. He called in another doctor to take a look; they'd never seen anyone recover so quickly!" exclaimed Dan.

"This has happened to a number of my clients in the past," I responded. "I was so hoping it would happen for you, too. When I hear your story, it gives me inspiration to keep doing this work! I'm absolutely convinced it makes a positive difference."

A month has passed. My friend continues to heal rapidly. While receiving radiation, he comes about once a week for Reiki sessions to prompt quick recovery of the vulnerable tissue and bones. We also hope he can begin to wear his facial prosthesis early. With reconstruction, Reiki, many prayers, and pure determination, Dan is optimistic and assures me, "I've still got a lot of livin' to do!"

Major studies have been done to determine if we can affect things, both living and nonliving, at a distance. According to engineers at Princeton University, in a twenty-five-year-long study, the human mind can affect the behavior and output of basic machines even from thousands of miles away. For example, we can make a coin-flipping machine produce more heads than tails simply by willing it to do so, There are generally only two chances in ten thousand that the outcomes are a simple coincidence. (David Johnson's report, *Mind over Matter*) I say, if we can affect machinery we can surely affect humans!

When We Don't Heal
Some Closing Insights

Even in modern times, with all of our medical technology, we are still asking, "What makes us sick and how can we get well?" Humankind has been searching for these answers since the beginning of time. As a seasoned nurse in general medicine and private practice, I have had the opportunity to observe thousands of medical cases and listen to countless personal testimonials by people who are seeking cures and healing. Certainly, there is no pat answer to this most complex issue, but a few revelations have come into my view.

One of the most enlightening experiences happened a few years ago. I got a referral from a doctor friend of mine. Pam came to see me because of escalating migraine headaches. During her intake interview, she told me she'd had the headaches for over fifteen years and was on narcotics and anti-seizure medications to control them. Recently she took a leave of absence from work due to drowsiness and poor memory, the side effects of her necessary drugs. She called me after the first Reiki session and was so surprised to have some pain relief right away. She was eager to make a second appointment and was planning to come back in a week. Time passed. No phone call. Pam never came again. I saw her several months later in town. I asked her how the headaches were. She clearly responded, "I still have migraines and they will *never* go away!" It was such an emphatic response. What I really heard her say was that she has **"MY"graines** and she was **not giving them up!** Pam had hinted she had a turbulent relationship at home, and I was certain the migraines were providing some sort of *secondary gain*. That gain may consciously or subconsciously relieve her from a responsibility in her life or relationship she is not ready to address. Maybe, somewhere in the future, she will be able to change her mind and resume therapy. I will hold that healing space open for her. Life can be hard and it insists on constant personal growth and change.

Another time, I saw Lynn, who had been on chemotherapy for years to treat lymphoma, a form of cancer, but never went into remission. She said all the others she knew in a similar situation had remissions. We had three Reiki sessions and a word kept intuitively returning to me. It was *worthy*. I asked her what that word meant to her. She thought about it, covered her face with her hands, and then burst into tears. She told me her religious upbringing taught her she was not worthy of anything good. Clearly she felt others were deserving, but not herself. She said, "I am not *worthy* to go into remission." After I offered her encouragement, she went home and received one more chemo treatment. A week later she called me. "For the first time, my lung cancer partially cleared. The next chemo dose will be cut in half!" We were both excited and Lynn promised to return for more Reiki. I never saw Lynn again. I spoke to her six months later. She said she just couldn't feel good about herself and resumed her old dose of chemo right after the last reduction. I was certain the source of Lynn's stubborn remission was low self-esteem. *Thoughts become things* echoed in my head. *It is Universal Law.* Perhaps because of such destructive early teachings, Lynn couldn't find the strength to open the door to wellness. I thought about what a beautiful soul she truly was, worthy of everything enjoyable. I knew *only she* could make the first move to discover that, and I wished her the best.

I have observed some clients and patients who haven't taken any personal responsibility for what was going wrong with their bodies. I have read that if we quit smoking, reduced alcohol consumption, and ate a healthy diet, doctor visits in this country would be reduced by seventy-five percent. Occasionally, people have told me all the brutal details of their despairing medical condition, but they have not taken the next responsible step—to make an appointment to move forward. In all honesty, talking and doing nothing more cannot move us out of our pain and onto our healing path. I feel humans are strong, resilient and courageous and once they decide to do so, can meet all the challenges of the earth plane. Unfortunately, so many remain asleep to who they really are.

Another client I recall came for Reiki for severe asthma. She had recently begun to wheeze and was very short of breath. The last asthma attack was so severe she nearly died before she could make it to the emergency room. Her prescribed medication had lost its therapeutic effect. Right after her first Reiki session she admitted to feeling lighter, had less tension in her chest, and was breathing better. As I watched her leave my office, I was horrified to see her light up a cigarette before she reached the parking lot. Our healing treatment was sabotaged and basically destroyed, and I felt a sense of sadness as she disappeared from sight.

Some of my friends believe in karma and explained that when we are ill we may be paying back debts owed from a previous life. After the debt is paid we reach Nirvana—the perfect state—and do not have to return to earth. Or maybe we are learning the hardest lessons this life can teach to stimulate personal growth and spiritual maturity. So many scenarios, so many things to think about.

I have often wondered if certain people come to earth as *teachers,* showing the rest of us how to deal with life's greatest challenges. My friend Tony went into renal failure after suffering from a rare vascular disease. He was on renal dialysis for ten years before he died from complications of surgery. Despite his condition, Tony loved life, was positive, upbeat, and pursued his professional opportunities. He seemed to focus on his *abilities,* not disabilities. I recall him choosing a vacation spot where he could also have dialysis—he took a trip to Arizona, got a treatment there, and enjoyed the warmth and beauty of the scenery, defying that disease to interfere. I think he had more good moments in his short forty years than many who live to be 100. When I attended his memorial service, everyone reported learning significant lessons from him, and some told me they were sure he was an angel.

No matter what the illness or how it came to be, the first step to getting better is *admitting there is a health problem.* Then the real challenge is to follow through with *action* to improve it. Consider these lifestyle adjustments as *power tools* for good health: *meditation, physical exercise, a positive attitude, wholesome food, good hygiene, enough rest, clothing from natural fibers, a home you resonate with, time for fun, and most important—love and friendship.* Love is the foundation for good health.

Finally, include energy therapy in your life. Take a class and learn more. Open up to the possibilities of a new paradigm and try a treatment for yourself! It could be the addition that finally heals you through a powerful combination of miracles, inspiration, and science.

Afterword

Miracles and inspiration are present every day, all around us, but we don't notice unless we look for them. In my practice, I have witnessed infertile women having beautiful babies, people going into remission from cancer, surgeries performed with almost no bleeding, all symptoms of emotional despair disappearing in one Reiki treatment, animals healing, and people positively affected through distance intention. Many times these healings cannot logically be explained. To me, they are *inspirations and miracles*. They are out there for all of us. To make them yours, *open up to the possibilities, reach out, and touch them... Get ready, Shift your consciousness, and Begin it now!*

Bibliography

American Heritage, *The American Heritage Book of Indians*, American Heritage Publishing Co., 1961.

Baginski, Bobo and Sharamon, Shalila, *Reiki, Universal Life Energy*, Mendocino, CA. LifeRhythm, 1988.

Barnett, Libbie and Chambers, Maggie, *Reiki, Energy Medicine*, Rochester, VT. Healing Arts Press, 1996.

Becker, Robert and Selden, Gary, *The Body Electric, Electromagnetism and the Foundation of Life,* New York, NY. Quill, 1985.

Benor, Daniel M.D., *Spiritual Healing, Scientific Validation of a Healing Revolution*, Southfield, MI. Vision Publication, 2001.

Brennan, Barbara, *Hands of Light, A Guide to Healing Through the Human Energy Field,* New York, NY. Bantam, 1987.

Dossey,Barbara, Keegan, Lynn, Guzzetta, Cathie, Kolkmeier, *Holistic Nursing, A Handbook for Practice*, Rockville, MD. Aspen,1988.

Dossey, Larry M.D., *Reinventing Medicine, Beyond Mind-Body to a New Era of Healing,* San Francisco, CA.. Harper, 1999.

Gerber, Richard, M.D., *Vibrational Medicine, Energy Healing and Spiritual Transformation,* New York, NY. Harper Collins, 2000.

Gordon, James S. M.D., *Manifesto for a New Medicine, Your Guide to Healing Partnerships and the Wise Use of Alternative Therapies,* Reading, MA. Peruses, 1996.

Gordon, Richard, *Your Healing Hands, The Polarity Experience,* Oakland, CA. Wingbow, 1978.

Hawkins, David R. M.D., PhD., *Power vs. Force, The Hidden Determinants of Human Behavior,* Carlsbad, CA. Hay House , 1995.

Honervogt, Tanmaya, *The Power of Reiki: An Ancient Hands-On Technique,* New York, NY. Henry Holt & Co., 1998.

Horan, Paula, *Empowerment Through Reiki, The Path to Personal and Global Transformation,* Twin Lakes, WI. Lotus Light,1990.

Kalweit, Holger, *Shamans, Healers and Medicine Men,* Boston and London. Shamballa, 1987.

La Farge, Oliver, *A Pictorial History of the American Indian,* New York, NY. Crown, 1970.

Lubeck, Walter, *Pendulum Healing Handbook, A Complete Guide on How to Use the Pendulum to Choose Appropriate Remedies for Healing Body, Mind, and Spirit,* Twin Lakes, WI. Lotus Light, 1998.

Motz, Julie, *Hands of Life.* New York, NY. Bantam Books, 1998.

Oschman, James L. PhD, *Energy Medicine, The Scientific Basis,* Philadelphia, PA. Harcourt Publishers, 2000.

Rahm, Rev. Harold, "St. Catherine Laboure and the Miraculous Medal," printed with ecclesiastical permission, The Blue Army of Our Lady of Fatima, Washington, NJ. (reference brochure, no date).

Stein, Diane, *"Essential Reiki, A Complete Guide To An Ancient Healing Art,"* Freedom, CA. Crossing Press, 1993.

Stein, Diane, *Natural Healing for Dogs and Cats,* Freedom, CA. Crossing Press, 1993.

Disclaimer: The information in this book is not medicine but about healing. It should not take the place of medical advice. In case of serious illness, consult your physician or health care provider.